Home Office (Fire Depart~

CW01022941

Fire Se.....

Drill Book

London Her Majesty's Stationery Office
1985

© *Crown copyright* 1985
First published 1949
Sixth edition (completely revised) 1985

ISBN 0 11 340804 8

Introduction

It should be clearly understood that the standard drills set out in this Drill Book are for the purpose of:

achieving uniformity in the basic training of personnel in the use of their appliances and equipment

ensuring that the appliances and equipment may be used with speed, efficiency, confidence and without confusion.

The drills include the use of appliances and fire-fighting equipment in general use in the Fire Service, and as soon as men become proficient, the standard drills will have served their purpose and more advanced training should be given. Nevertheless the specific skills and safety measures learnt in basic drills should be maintained, without exception, in more advanced stages of training.

The Fire Service is a hazardous profession—it is therefore essential that every person at an incident is so well trained in standard procedures that they can also cope with the unexpected dangers which occur. Training and practice can be carried out in comparatively safe conditions but, at a real incident, the situation may be very different.

For advanced training it is important that fireground conditions are simulated as far as possible, and fireground procedures introduced. This training should take the form of fire situation exercises, and men should be encouraged to use initiative under varying conditions, including the use of more than one appliance and several items of equipment in combination. This form of training has the advantage of flexibility in that it can be adapted to local conditions.

Training should also be given in the use and application of equipment to deal with the various special services to which men are likely to be called.

Safety is the concern of every member of the Fire Service.
In this book various drills and other activities are described—doing them *correctly* i.e. Using the specified methods and precautions will lead towards greater safety.

Particular safety aspects are highlighted within each section but there are some general points which are covered in "Notes on drills (general)" Page 1.

Reference in this book to the male person should be construed as applying, as appropriate, to the female person also. The ranks of junior firewoman, firewoman and leading firewoman have been introduced by the Fire Services (Appointments and Promotion) (Amendment) Regulations 1976 to equate with the ranks of junior fireman, fireman and leading fireman, and references to the latter should, where appropriate, be construed as references to the former.

The Home Office is indebted to all those who have assisted in the preparation of this work.

Contents

Part I

Appliance and miscellaneous drills page 1

Preliminary detail to drills 20

Hydrant and hose drills 20

Appliance drills 21

Hose drills 24

Pump drills 34

Squad drill and saluting   202

Squad drill   202

Appliance and miscellaneous drills

Notes on drills (general)

Safeguards

1. The wearing of personal jewellery (for example rings and watches,) can be hazardous, such items should be removed before taking part in drills. Rings which cannot be removed should be covered with adhesive tape.

2. Neckerchiefs, if worn, should *not* be knotted, they should just be folded around the neck and covered by the tunic collar.

3. Helmets must be worn by all personnel.

4. Fire gear, particularly boots, should be kept in good order and repair.

5. The officer in charge should ensure that any drill which is being carried out is performed in a safe manner, using accepted practices. He should, for example, make sure that men working aloft check that no personnel are below when dropping objects e.g. a line and that they give the warning 'stand-from-under'.

6. Each member taking part in a drill is responsible for carrying out his function in such a way that neither his own safety or that of any other member is put at risk. The driver, for example, should:

(a) before leaving the driving seat, ensure that the handbrake is firmly on and the gear-lever is in the correct position;

(b) before driving off, ensure that the appliance is correctly stowed, all doors are properly closed and that the power take-off is disengaged.

(c) before reversing, ensure that a man who can be seen by him is stationed at the rear to act as a guide and to make sure that the area is clear and safe. Remember that verbal signals may not be heard so a suitable hand-signal should be pre-arranged. The guide must always remain in view of the driver. The signals recommended by the Road Transport Industry Board are shown in Figs 1−5.

1

(d) switch off the engine immediately on completion of a drill.

7. The officer in charge of the drill should ensure that each man:

(a) understands *what* he is to do and

(b) understands *why* he is to do it.

8. Every man should also fully understand the duties of other members of the crew—good teamwork is essential on the fireground, particularly if conditions are bad. The officer in charge should therefore use the 'change-round' command to ensure that members of the same crew occupy the various drill positions.

1.ADVANCE

Use the right hand and forearm vertically, palm away from driver 'drawing him onwards and calling "come on" if necessary.

2. REVERSE

Use both hands and forearms
with palms facing the driver
'pushing' him back and
calling 'go on' if necessary.

3. CHANGE DIRECTION

Extend arm and clenched fist sideways from the shoulder in the direction the REAR of the vehicle is to be steered.

4. STOP

Raise the right hand and arm vertically, palm facing the driver, fingers extended but together.

Shout "STOP" loud and clear.

5. CLEARANCE

Raise arms above head, palms inwards, indicating amount of clearance between vehicle and loading bay, obstacles, etc.

9. If the officer in charge decides to undertake training in the hours of darkness and/or under adverse weather conditions then he should introduce such extra safety precautions as are necessary.

10. An officer-in-charge should make the maximum use of B.A. in training but wearers should not be overtaxed by, for example, having to run up ladders.

11. Men should be encouraged to use their initiative under varying conditions, including the use of more than one appliance and several items of equipment in combination.

12. All equipment needed for a drill should be available before starting.

13. Equipment on which the safety of life depends (such as lines) should be tested before carrying out drills involving them.

14. Drill towers should be used carefully, in particular:

(a) Dry risers in drill towers should not be tested or used in a drill whilst other tower drills are in progress.

(b) staircases, landings, windows, etc. must be checked and cleared of obstructions and objects not required before drills take place.

15. For all rescue drills the officer-in-charge shall ensure that all agreed procedures, specified in Home Office Fire Service Circulars and Dear Chief Officer/Firemaster Letters, are complied with. An experienced member of the Brigade (to be known as the Safety Officer) should: .

(a) be stationed on the floor of the drill tower from which the rescue is to be effected (or in an appropriate position at whichever site is chosen for the drill) close to the participants in the rescue;

(b) satisfy himself that all appropriate precautions have been taken;

(c) stop the drill if he observes any unsafe activity taking place (although the officer in charge retains overall responsibility);

(d) where live rescues are being carried out, ensure that the safety device is properly attached to an anchorage fitted to a drill tower;

(e) ensure that, during drills and practices of lowering a fireman for the purpose of carrying out an operational task, a turntable ladder or hydraulic platform (not an escape or extension ladder) is used as the anchorage if a fixed anchorage is not conveniently positioned;

(f) ensure that the Check Test (Standard Test No. 13) is applied to the safety device;

(g) ensure that the belt of the safety device is properly fitted and adjusted;

(h) ensure that the line of the safety device is properly secured to the belt.

16. When taking drills, the officer in charge should stand so that he can see and be seen and can hear and be heard whilst the whole drill is carried out.

17. All commands should be clearly audible—not only for training purposes, but also in case warnings such as "STILL!" or "stand from under" are needed.

18. All personnel must be aware of the meaning, purpose and correct procedure for using such warnings. (See page 9.)

19. On completion of any drill No. 1 will report to the officer in charge "Drill complete." Other commands are listed in the next section.

Words of Command

The following words of command are to be used in drills and, where applicable, at fires. A dash indicates the pause between the cautionary and the executive parts of the command. A_indicates that the words are given as a single order.

Words of command

Command	Action or meaning
STILL!	Only to be used in an emergency (i.e. to prevent an accident) and then with maximum force; the crew remain perfectly still exactly where they are. It may be given by any member of the crew as well as by the officer in charge.
REST!	To be used, if necessary, by the instructor when carrying out a drill to point out a mistake; the crew remain still.
WELL!	To indicate that the position desired has been reached e.g. when extending or lowering a ladder.
As_you_were	Cancels an order previously given; men resume their previous positions.
Carry_on	Given after 'Rest' or 'Still'; the crew carry on with what they were doing.
Change—round	As many members of the crew as necessary dismount and, moving one place in an anti-clockwise direction, take up their new riding positions so that (e.g. in a 4−man crew), No. 1 becomes No. 3, No. 3 becomes No. 4, No. 4 becomes No. 2 and No. 2 becomes No. 1.

This change round should be used to ensure that crew members know each position and the duty to perform at that position. The crew should always be renumbered after the change. When carrying out appliance drill the command should only be given when a crew is in the 'Mount' position.

Command	Action or meaning
Counterbalance	To lift up the rear end of an escape to replace the escape on the appliance.
Crews—number	No. 1 of the first crew calls 'one', No. 1 of the second crew calls 'two', and so on until all crews are numbered.
Depress	To decrease the angle of turntable ladder with the horizontal, or reduce the height of the cage of a hydraulic platform above the ground.
Dis—mount	The crew dismount from the appliance and return to the 'Fall in' position.
Elevate	To increase the angle of a ladder with the horizontal, or increase the height of the cage of a hydraulic platform above the ground.
Extend	To increase the overall length of a ladder.
Extend to lower	To raise the extending portion of a ladder to clear the pawls for lowering.
Fall—in	The named crew turn smartly to the right, pause, and moving at the double, fall in three paces to the rear of, and facing, the appliance, and stand to attention.
Fall—out	The crew turn to the right, pause, break away and fall in on the left of the squad in single rank and stand at ease.
Get_to_work	The crew carry out the drill as detailed.
Head_in	To move the head of a ladder towards a building.
Head_out	To move the head of a ladder away from a building.

Command	Action or meaning
Heelboard	To indicate when descending that the heelboard at the foot of the escape is the next step downwards.
Heel_in	To move the heel of a ladder into the building.
Heel_out	To move the heel of a ladder away from a building.
House	To reduce the overall length of a ladder.
Knock_off	To close down the water supply at the pump delivery and/or the hydrant.
Launch	(Escapes with 'push-in' mountings). The crew push forward on the carriage frame and secure the escape in its mounting.
Make_up	The crew make up and re-stow all gear.
Mount	The crew mount the appliance. The riding position of each member will depend on the design and other factors, but No. 2 will always be the driver and No. 1 will, whenever possible, sit in the seat on his near side.
Pawls	To indicate when descending a ladder that the pawls are fitted on the next round below and the feet should be placed towards the centre of the round.

This command (along with ''step in'' and ''step out'') should be used during drills to accustom men to the procedure, particularly when performing rescue drills.

The order should be given when the leading foot reaches the round immediately above the hazard.

Pitch	To erect a ladder against a building; e.g. 'Pitch to the third floor.'
Slip	To remove a ladder from the appliance.

Command	Action or meaning
Stand_from_under	To be used by anybody who has to lower equipment or drop debris from a height when there is a risk that it might strike someone. When lowering items the man should ensure that no personnel are below. It should also be used when equipment is accidentally dropped from a height.
Step in	To indicate that the overlap of extensions is reached when descending ladder with extensions on the upper side (see Note on "Pawls").
Step_out	To indicate that the overlap of extensions is reached when descending ladder with extensions on the underside (see Note on "Pawls").
Train	To move the head of a turntable ladder or a hydraulic platform by rotating the turntable.
Under—run	To raise a ladder from a horizontal to a vertical position and vice versa.
Water_on	To turn on the hydrant, open a delivery valve on the pump, etc. according to the drill being performed.
Note	One special command for training purposes is, "As far as detailed—carry on". This should be used so that a long procedure or one with a lot of detail can be built up in stages.

Fire Service Signals

1. Pumping Signals

Whenever practicable the best way to convey orders is by messenger, an alternative is to send radio messages direct to the pump operator. Whistles must not be used.

There are occasions when messages or commands may be passed by signal—equally there are times when they could result in confusion or danger. Examples of when visual signals should *not* be used include:

(1) Where two or more pumps are at work and a signal that is intended for one pump might be obeyed by another pump.

(2) Instructions to raise or lower pressure when more than one branch is working from the same pump.

(3) At night or in poor visibility.

2. Visual signals

Order	Arm Signal
Water on	The arm is raised sideways over the head to its fullest extent and lowered smartly to the side. This signal should never be given until a branch is manned and the branchman is ready and prepared.
Knock off	The right arm is extended horizontally, swung across the chest and back again.
Increase pressure	As for 'Water on' but repeated several times. Pump operators should increase pressure by 1 bar, unless otherwise instructed.
Reduce pressure	One arm is extended horizontally from the shoulder and the other arm is raised vertically. The pressure should be reduced by 1 bar, unless otherwise instructed.
Make up all gear	Both arms are extended outwards and dropped to the sides.
All men report to the officer	The right arm is swung round the head and then the hand is placed flat on the head.
Acknowledgement of signals	All visual signals should be acknowledged by repeating the signal.

3. Line signals

There may be occasions when a fireman has to be lowered down a shaft, a well, or over a cliff in order to effect a rescue or for other reasons. In the absence of other means of communication, e.g. breathing apparatus communication equipment, the fireman should be lowered on the one line and have a second line attached to him for signalling purposes.

The following signals should be used:

Signal on line	Given by wearer	Given by attendant
1 pull	I am all right.	Are you all right?
2 pulls	Pay out more line.	I am paying out more line.
2 pulls-pause-2 pulls	Stop lowering.	I am ceasing lowering.
3 pulls	Haul in slack line, or Haul up.	I am hauling in slack line, or I am hauling up.
Repeated, sharp pulls	Danger—help me out.	Danger—I am hauling up as quickly as possible.

4. Evacuation of premises signals

The signal recommended by the CFBAC for the evacuation of premises is repeated short blasts on a whistle of the Acme 'Thunderer' type. Whistles should be carried by all leading firemen and ranks above; in addition, a whistle should always be available for the officer in charge of an appliance. Whistles should be used only for the standard evacuation signal and not for any other purpose.

All firemen hearing repeated short blasts from a whistle should make their way as quickly as possible out of the premises, but the withdrawal should be orderly so that a dangerous situation is not caused.

5. Warning signals-railways

Special warning horns are carried on certain appliances. The approach of trains should be signalled by blasts on the warning horns.

Standard knots

Definition:- A knot may be defined as the interlacement of any form of cordage in specific patterns for the purpose of stopping ends, joining ends together, forming bights or securing equipment etc.

Standard terms

There are a number of standard terms for use in describing parts of a knot, etc. and the following should be learnt and understood by every fireman.

Bend	To fasten a line to another line or to an object.
Bight	The looped or loose part of a line between the two ends.
Hitch	A simple fastening of a line to some object by passing the line round the object and crossing one part over the other.
Running Part	The moving part of a line which is loose and used to hoist or lower.
Running End	The free end of a line.
Seizing	The binding together of two or more ropes.
Standing Part	The part of a line which is fixed.
Whipping	The binding of the end of a line with twine to prevent it unlaying.

The following is a list of knots, bends and hitches with which every fireman should be familiar. He should be able to make the more important ones whilst blindfold. These given below are the basic knots for normal Fire Service purposes (many of these will be used in the drills which follow). The Manual of Firemanship should be used as a reference for information on additional knots that may be required.

Standard name	Detail
Overhand Knot	Sometimes known as a thumb knot. Used as a simple stopper and tied at each end in lengths of burst hose when laid out.
Half Hitch	The basis of a number of knots. Used extensively in conjunction with other knots for securing suction, etc.
Reef Knot	Used to join two lines of equal thickness
Double Sheet bend	A secure method of joining two lines of unequal thickness.
Clove Hitch	Used to secure a line to any round object.

Standard name	Detail

Rolling Hitch
Used to secure a line to any round object so that the knot will not slip along the object when a sideways pull is applied.

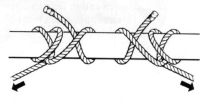

Round Turn and two Half Hitches
Used to secure a line to any round object.

Bowline
Also known as the single bowline. A non-slipping noose used for a large variety of purposes.

Running Bowline
A bowline in the form of a running noose.

Chair Knot Used as a sling to lower an
insensible person.

Barrel Hitch Used for raising or
lowering barrels.

Preliminary detail to drills

Notes on preliminary detail

There are certain preliminaries which are common to all drills—they are covered at the start of this section. They apply to any modern appliance according to the number of men in the crew (and the particular drill).

For each of these drills crews should be formed and numbered in the following way:

> **'Formation of crews'.** Men fall in single rank and number from the right in threes, fours or fives (depending on the particular drill). Each group of three, four or five is a crew.

> **'Crews Number'.** Number 1 of the first crew calls '*one*', Number 1 of the second crew calls '*two*' and so on until all crews are numbered.

A specific crew can now be ordered to 'fall in'—taking up the positions as specified for each drill. In the descriptions of each drill it is assumed that

(a) the crews have been formed and numbered;
(b) the crews will 'fall in' at the double and
(c) after falling in they will take up their dressing on number 1 who will be on the left.

Preliminary detail to hydrant and hose drills. (Four men)　　　Drill PD1

On the command '**Number . . . crew, fall in**' the named crew fall in three paces from and facing the equipment.

They should be in the order shown below:

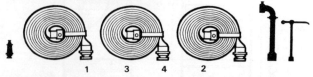

1　　3　　4　　2

'Change Round'. No. 1 doubles round the back of the crew taking up position and becoming No. 2, and other three members of the crew each take a pace to their left. No. 3 becomes No. 1, No. 4 becomes No. 3 and No. 2 becomes No. 4.

> *Note:* After a 'change round', the crew should be renumbered to identify them in their new positions.

Preliminary detail to Appliance drills (Three men)

'**Number . . . Crew, fall in**'. The named crew fall in three paces to the rear of and facing the appliance in the order shown:

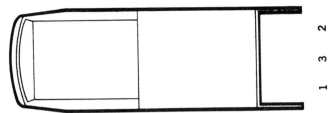

'**Mount**'. Nos. 1 and 3 turn half left, No. 2 turns half right and, moving at the double, take up their riding positions on the appliance, No. 2 in the driver's seat, No. 1 on the left of No. 2 and No. 3 according to accommodation and where possible behind No. 1, as shown below.

Special care should be taken when mounting or dismounting and the safety measures on pages 1–8 should be borne in mind.

'**Change Round**'. All members of the crew dismount and, moving in an anti-clockwise direction, take up their new riding positions so that No. 1 becomes No. 3, No. 3 becomes No. 2, and No. 2 becomes No. 1.

Note: After a 'change round' the crew should be renumbered to identify them in their new positons.

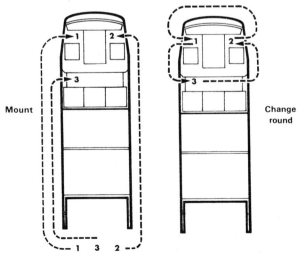

Preliminary detail to appliance drills (Four men)   Drill PD3

'**Number . . . crew fall in**'. The named crew fall in three paces to the rear of and facing the appliance in the order as shown below:

'**Mount**'. Nos. 1 and 3 turn half left, Nos. 2 and 4 turn half right and, moving at the double, take up their riding positions on the appliance, No. 2 in the driver's seat, No. 1 on the left of No. 2, Nos. 3 and 4 according to accomodation, with, where possible, No. 3 behind No. 1 and No. 4 behind No. 2.

'**Change Round**'. As many members of the crew as necessary dismount and, moving in an anti-clockwise direction, take up their new riding positions so that No. 1 becomes No. 3, No. 3 becomes No. 4, No. 4 becomes No. 2, and No. 2 becomes No. 1.

> *Note:* After a 'change round' the crew should be renumbered to identify them in their new positions.

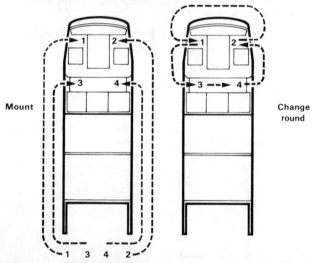

Mount   Change round

Preliminary detail to appliance drills (Five men)   Drill PD4

'**Number . . . crew fall in**'. The named crew fall in three paces to the rear of the facing the appliance, as shown below:

'**Mount**'. Nos. 1, 3 and 5 turn half left, Nos. 2 and 4 turn half right and, moving at the double, take up their riding positions on the appliance, No. 2 in the driver's seat, No. 1 on the left of No. 2, Nos. 3, 4 and 5 according to accomodation, with, where possible, No. 3 behind No. 1, and No. 4 behind No. 2.

'Change Round'. As many members of the crew as necessary dismount and moving in an anti-clockwise direction, take up their new riding positions so that No. 1 becomes No. 3, No. 3 becomes No. 5, No. 5 becomes No. 4, No. 4 becomes No. 2 and No. 2 becomes No. 1.

Note: After a 'change round' the crew should be renumbered to identify them in their new positions.

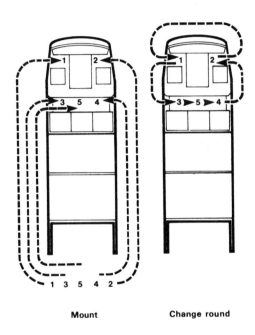

Mount　　　　　**Change round**

Hose drills

Notes on hose drills

As well as the preliminary details described in the last section, there are some specific points which apply to all Hose Drills.

1. Immediately after shipping a standpipe the hydrant valve should be opened momentarily to clear the outlet of any obstruction.

2. Hydrant covers should be placed in a safe position across the pit when the hydrant is in use. Some form of warning light should be placed in position when visibility is poor.

3. Hose rolled on the female coupling. (Safety aspects are underlined).

(a) When rolled hose is being carried before it is run out, the male coupling should be allowed to hang down about 300mm from the front of the roll.

(b) Before running out the first length of rolled hose, the male coupling should be connected either to a pump delivery or to a standpipe, or should be secured by a member of the crew putting his foot on it. If this is not possible, a short length, sufficient to prevent dragging, should be spun off the roll and laid on the ground before moving forward.
Couplings and hose must not be dragged along the ground.

(c) To run out rolled hose, the lugs of the female coupling (which are at the centre of the roll) are taken one in each hand, the hose is held chest high and is allowed to revolve around the lugs and pay out on the right hand side of the body. (Plate 5 (left))

(d) A man who has already run out a length of hose should keep hold of the female coupling with his right hand—he should then take hold of the male coupling of the next length in his left hand and make the connection.

(e) On reaching the scene of the 'fire' any excess hose should be laid out in the form of a bight, as illustrated.

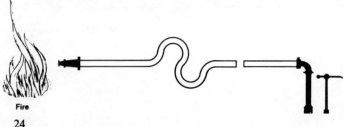

Fire

24

4. Dutch-rolled hose.

(a) Dutch-rolled hose should be carried under the arm, with the top of the roll securely in the armpit and the hand supporting the bottom of the roll. The couplings should be within a few millimetres of each other and should hang down just behind the hand.

(b) To run out, the hose immediately above the couplings should be gripped and the other hand brought to the top of the roll, as illustrated. (Plate 5 (right))

(c) Both hands thrust the hose forward so that it unrolls in the direction of the 'fire'.

(d) The male coupling should be handed to the man making the connection and the female coupling taken in the direction of the 'fire until the hose has been laid out.

5. Flaked hose

(a) Flaked hose is often made up in trays, may already be coupled to the pump and generally has a branch fitted so that it can be run out without delay.

(b) All the hose must be withdrawn from the tray before water is turned on.

(c) The amount of hose varies but is usually at least two lengths. 45mm diameter hose is frequently used because of ease of handling.

(d) The hose should be run out by gripping the branch and running towards the 'fire'.

6. Branch holding

(a) Whenever possible there should be two men on the branch before the full flow is allowed to develop.

(b) The man standing on the left should allow the hose to come up under his right arm. His right hand should be under the coupling. His left hand should be on the top of the branch.

(c) The man on the right should place his right hand on the top of the branch and his left hand under the hose.

(d) Both men should exert a forward and downward pressure, (Plate 6).

(e) **Safety**
    (i) The instructor should ensure that the crew appreciate the influence of pressure and of nozzle diameter on the reaction of the branch.

(ii) As far as possible, the last 3m of the hose to a branch should be kept in a straight line.

(iii) When working on an upper floor or flat roof, sufficient hose should be handed up to enable 1 or 2m to be placed on the floor or on the roof. This will help to stop the weight of the charged line affecting the branchman.

(iv) Should a charged branch get out of control the order 'knock off' should be given immediately. Control of a charged branch can only be achieved by crawling along the line of hose towards the branch, slowly limiting the movements until control can be regained.

(v) If a branch becomes out of control on a ladder, an immediate warning should be given to personnel working in close proximity.

(vi) In all drills where a line of hose is to be taken aloft, the hose coupling at the heel of the ladder or base of the building should be left uncoupled until the branchman gives the order 'Water On'. This means that, for example, the branchline cannot be charged before the branchman is in a secure position.

(vii) When a length of hose is to be hauled up outside a building, the line must be arranged so that it takes the full weight of the hose. The weight of a charged length of hose leading into the upper floors of a building must be taken by means of a becket, sling or line secured to the ladder or some convenient object on the building.

7. Changing branchmen

(a) To relieve the man on the left:
  (i) the relieving branchman will approach from the left side. He should place his left hand on that of the original branchman, who will then draw his hand away.
  (ii) the relieving man should then turn to face the fire and place his right hand in position under the coupling, the original man should then step to the rear, clear of the branch.

(b) To relieve the man on the right:
  (i) the relieving branchman approaches from the right, placing his right hand on top of the original man's hand, who then draw his hand away.
  (ii) the relieving man then turns to face the fire and should place his left hand under the hose and the original man will step to the rear.

8. Making up

(a) A hydrant must always be turned off slowly to prevent water hammer.

(b) When breaking couplings the source of supply should be faced with the male coupling held between the knees. This prevents it dropping to the ground and being damaged.

(c) **Safety**
   (i) Stand clear when releasing blank caps, collecting breeching or couplings of charged hose.
   (ii) When making up hose that has been working aloft the head of water should be released by breaking the nearest coupling to the branch outside the building.
   (iii) Gloves should be worn when making up hose which has been laid over debris.

(d) Prior to underrunning, hose should be laid out flat, straight and free from kinks which would trap water. On level ground hose should be underrun from the male end. On sloping ground it should be underrun from the higher coupling. Hose should not be walked along to get rid of water as this can cause severe damage to the fibres.

(e) After underrunning, the hose should be rolled up starting with the female coupling, the first few turns being made tightly. Then, by pushing with both hands together and on top of the roll, the length should be completed, keeping the coil even and flat. When the male coupling is reached, the hose should be rolled over it so that the coupling comes out on top. Coils of hose must not be jumped on to get the coil even.

(f) When making up burst lengths of hose, the overhand knot should be removed and the hose rolled on the male coupling.

General

1. All messages e.g. 'Water on', 'Knock off' should be repeated back to the originator/messenger.

2. When referring to hose, whether suction or delivery, the first length is the length nearest the pump or hydrant.

Hose drills

Laying one line of hose from a hydrant (Four men)   **Drill H1**

Preliminary detail: As given in PD1.

'Get to work'. No. 2 takes a standpipe, hydrant key and bar, removes the hydrant cover and ships the standpipe and key.

For Hose Rolled on the Female Coupling. No. 4 takes a length of hose, places the male coupling on the ground approximately half a metre behind the hydrant and after No. 2 has secured it with his foot, runs it out towards the fire.

He is followed, two or three paces behind, by No. 3 who takes a length of hose, carrying it under his right arm.

When No. 4 has run out his hose, No. 3 overtakes, No. 4 taking the male coupling as he passes. No. 4 then makes the connection. No. 3 lays out his hose and, holds the female coupling in his right hand.

No. 1 tucks the branch under his left arm, nozzle pointing downwards and toward the rear, carries a length of hose under his right arm and follows two or three paces behind No. 3.

When No. 3 stops, No. 1 continues and, as he passes, No. 3 takes the male coupling and makes the connection. No. 1 continues until the hose is run out, then keeping hold of the female coupling in his left hand, he takes hold of the branch in his right and makes the connection.

Note: At a fire, as far as possible, hose should be run out on the pavement or close to the side of the road.

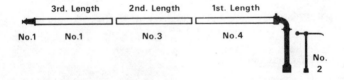

For Dutch-rolled hose. No. 4 takes a length of hose and throws it forward from the hydrant in the direction of the fire, hands the male coupling to No. 2 and then lays the hose out.

No. 2 connects it to the standpipe.

No. 3 takes a length of hose and, carrying it under the right arm with his right hand supporting it in front of the couplings, follow two or three paces behind No. 4.

When No. 4 has run out his hose, No. 3 throws his length forward, hands the male coupling to No. 4, who makes the connection, and runs forward with the female coupling.

No. 1 takes the branch in his left hand and a length of hose under his right arm and follows two or three paces behind No. 3.

When No. 3 has run out his hose, No. 1 throws his length forward and hands the male coupling to No. 3.

For both types of roll. As the hose is run out, Nos. 3 and 4 follow No. 1 to the branch, No. 4 seeing that the hose is free from kinks.

When Nos. 1 and 3 are on the branch No. 1 sends back No. 4 with the message *'Water on'*. No. 4 delivers the message to No. 2, who turns on the hydrant.

No. 4 returns to the branch, and generally assists.

'Knock off' or **'Knock off and make up'**. No. 1 sends back No. 4 with the message: *'Knock off'* or *'knock off and make up'*.

'Make up' No. 1 returns the branch, No. 2 unships the standpipe, makes up the hydrant, and returns all the gear. All members of the crew underrun and make up hose. When all the gear is made up, No. 1 reports to the officer in charge.

Adding a length of hose (Four men) Drill H2

> *Note:* It will be assumed that the hose has been run out as in Drill H1.

Unless otherwise ordered when working in the open, a length of hose is always added between the branch and the last coupling. When working in a building, the length is usually added at the first coupling outside the building.

'Get to work'. No. 1 sends No. 4 back to obtain a length of hose. No. 4 lays out the hose at the connection indicated in the form of a bight or parallel to the hose line, as dictated by local conditions.

As soon as the hose is laid out and ready for connection No. 4 gives No. 2 the order *'Knock off'*. As soon as the flow ceases, No. 4 breaks the couplings and inerts the new length.

Having ensured that No. 1 is ready, he then doubles to No. 2 with the message *'Water on'*.

When the length of hose is added at the branch, No. 1 removes the branch and connects it to the added length.

Nos. 1 & 3

'Knock off' or **'Knock off and make up''** as H1

Removing a length of hose
(Four men)

Drill H3

Note: It will be assumed that the hose has been run out as in Drill H1.

'Get to work'. No. 1 sends back No. 4 to No. 2 with the message *'Knock off'*. Immediately the message is given, No. 4 doubles back to the first coupling behind the branch. As soon as the flow ceases. No. 1 disconnects the branch and No. 4, breaks the connection and assists No. 1 to recouple the branch at its new position.

No. 1 sends back No. 4 with the message *'Water on'*. No. 4 subsequently returns to the branch and makes up the surplus hose.

'Knock off' or **'Knock off and make up'** as in H1.

Replacing a burst length of hose
(Four men)

Drill H4

Note: It will be assumed that the hose has been run out as in Drill H1.

'Get to work'. On the order of No. 1, No. 4 takes a length of hose and runs it out alongside the damaged length.

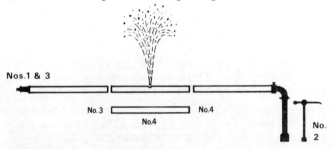

He then gives No. 2 the order *'Knock off'*. At the same time No. 3 doubles to the burst length and, as soon as the flow ceases, assists No. 4 to disconnect the burst length and to insert the new length.

No. 3 then doubles to the branch and informs No. 1 that the new length is in position.

No. 4 returns to No. 2, with the message *'Water on'*, and then ties an overhand knot in each end of the damaged length.

Note: When a burst length of hose is made up, the overhand knots should be removed and the hose rolled up on the male coupling.

Getting a branch to work on a roof or upper floor (Four men)

Preliminary detail. As given in PD1.

'Get to work'. No. 1 takes a branch, a length of hose and a long line and doubles to the building. He runs out the hose in a bight outside the building then connects the branch to the hose, laying down the branch at the point where it is to be hoisted. Meanwhile No. 2 takes a standpipe, key and bar, removes the hydrant cover and ships the standpipe and key.

No. 4 takes a length of hose and runs it out from the hydrant towards the building. No. 3 takes a length of hose and runs it out from the first length and then lays the female coupling adjacent, but not connected, to the male coupling of the length run out by No. 1.

No. 1 then takes the line and accompanied by No. 3 enters the building, goes to the roof or window opening and lowers the line down the face of the building. No. 4 secures the line to the hose by means of a rolling hitch about 3 metres from the branch. He then forms a clove hitch on the line, about half a metre from the rolling

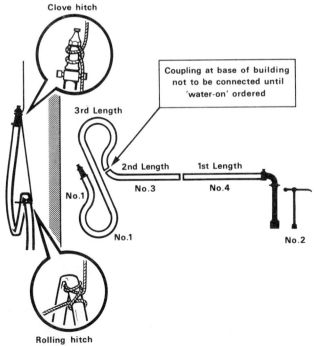

Clove hitch

Coupling at base of building not to be connected until 'water-on' ordered

3rd Length

2nd Length   1st Length

No.3   No.4

No.1

No.1

No.2

Rolling hitch

31

hitch, and passes it over the narrowest part of the branch underneath the nozzle to ensure that the tension is on the line and not the hose.

As soon as the line is secured Nos. 1 and 3 haul up the hose, No. 4 guiding it up the face of the building. When sufficent hose has been hauled up, the clove hitch is removed from the branch and the line is made fast at the most convenient position. The rolling hitch securing the hose should lie about half a metre below the coping or window sill when the line is secured to the building.

Meanwhile No. 4 positions himself on the ground so that he can see where the hose enters the building.

When ready, No. 1 orders *'Water on'* No. 3 then doubles to the point where the hose enters the building and passes the message to No. 4 by hand signal or by word of mouth, and then returns to the branch. No. 4 connects the couplings at the base of the building, and passes the message to No. 2 who turns on the hydrant. No. 4 then joins Nos. 1 and 3 at the branch.

'Knock off' or **'Knock off and make up'**. No. 1 sends back No. 4 with the message *'Knock off'* or *'knock off and make up'*.

'Make up' No. 2 turns off the hydrant, breaks the pressure-release coupling of the standpipe and makes up the hydrant gear. No. 4 breaks the coupling nearest the foot of the building and guides the hose as it is lowered. No. 3 hauls up the hose so that the rolling hitch is above the coping or windowsill. No. 1 secures the branch with a clove hitch then unties the line and lowers the hose and branch to No. 4. No. 1 then drops his end of the line and descends with No. 3, both assisting No. 4 to make up the hose.

When all gear is made up No. 1 reports to the officer in charge.

Dividing a line of hose into two with a dividing breeching (Five men)   Drill H6

Note: It is assumed that hose has been run out as in Drill H1 using four men. A fifth man must be added to the crew as two branches are involved and two men are needed for each branch in addition to the man at the hydrant.

'Get to work'. No. 5 provides a dividing breeching and No. 4 a length of hose and branch. No. 5 doubles to the coupling where the line is to be divided.

No. 4 runs out his hose from the position where the breeching is to be inserted, connects the branch and takes charge of it. No. 5 connects the male coupling into the breeching before placing it on the ground.

When all is ready No. 2 knocks off on the order of No. 5. No. 5 breaks the hose line, inserts the breeching reconnects the hose and orders *'Water on'*. He then assists No. 4 at the second branch.

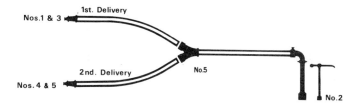

Removing a dividing breeching (Five men)   Drill H7

'Get to work'. No. 5 doubles to the breeching and orders No. 2 to *'Knock off'*. As soon as the flow ceases he disconnects the breeching, reconnects the length which is to continue at work and orders *'Water on'*. No. 4 then disconnects and returns his branch, No. 5 returns the breeching. Both numbers make up and return surplus hose.

Pump drills

Notes on operation and use of pumps

1. Safety

In order to ensure maximum safety in operating and using pumps the following points must be followed:

(a) When starting pumps or vehicles using a starting handle keep the thumb in line with the fingers and ensure that the handle is in the lower position when commencing the swing.

(b) Fold the carrying and starting handles on light portable pumps inwards before getting to work.

(c) Four men where appropriate should be used to remove a portable pump from an appliance and transport it. They should use the correct lifting techniques as described on page 215, the mounting frame where applicable, should be rehoused within the appliance.

(d) When working from underground tanks do not remove the cover until ready to drop the suction into the tank. Place the cover in a safe position, clear of operations. Where necessary erect a temporary guard to the manhole and use warning lights at night.

On making-up, withdraw suction hose and replace the manhole cover immediately, check that the cover fits evenly and does not 'rock'.

(e) Never remove a header tank cap whilst the engine is running.

(f) Exhaust fumes from a pump operating in a confined space can be lethal. Always make arrangements to disperse fumes before starting the pump. Take into account the wind direction.

(g) *Never* connect delivery hose to pumps fitted with exhaust gas ejector priming system until priming is completed.

If it is necessary to have a delivery open to prime, the pump operator should then prime from the side. When priming is complete, the first line of delivery hose should be connected to another *closed* pump delivery valve—when this is opened it will allow the original delivery to be closed ready for normal use.

(h) Whenever praticable in operations and always in training, the pump operator should position himself where he can see the pump gauges and see the branchmen or alternatively see the officer in charge of the drill or other member of the crew detailed to relay signals.

(j) If the pump operator sees a branch get out of control he should:

    (i) Immediately close the throttle.

    (ii) Close the delivery.

(k) (i) Any message for *'water on'* should also include the number of the delivery, the pump pressure required and the position of the branch, all messages being repeated to the sender before and after delivery. The pressure asked for should be that required at the pump.

    (ii) On the order *'Knock off'* the pump operator will shut down the appropriate deliveries but all equipment is left in position. On the order *'Knock off and make up'* the pump operator also disengages the pump and all equipment is made up as detailed in the drill.

    (iii) When deliveries are opened or closed the engine speed should be adjusted to avoid decreasing or increasing the flow and pressure at other branches supplied by the same pump.

(l) When making up a pump which has been working from open water, the suction joint at the pump should first be loosened; this will allow air to enter and the suction to empty.

The suction should then be lifted out of the water, disconnected at the pump inlet, and the other joints should be broken in turn, working towards the strainer. No. 2 should ensure that the delivery valves are closed.

(m) Remember: Stand clear when releasing a blank cap from a spare delivery of a pump. Even though the valve is shut, there may be sufficient leakage to build up a pressure high enough to project the cap violently from the delivery and cause injury.

Never release couplings, pressure release couplings or collecting heads from hose or pumps whilst they are under pressure.

When making up hose after working aloft, first release the pressure at the pump and then at the couplings at the base of the building.

(n) Remember: In all drills where a line of hose has to be taken aloft the hose coupling at the base of the ladder or building should be left uncoupled until the branchman gives the order *'Water on'*. This is to ensure that the branchman is not endangered by the branchline being charged before he is in a secure position.

2. General

(a) It should be noted that the deliveries are referred to by numbers starting from the nearside.

On centrally mounted deliveries the numbers start from the forward nearside delivery, and run anticlockwise.

(b) To join two lengths of suction, two men should stand face to face gripping the suction between the knees, each man using one wrench which should be held to obtain maximum leverage (Plate 7).

(c) The universal type of suction wrench in Plate 3 will fit all sizes of suction coupling. The eye in the lever arm should be placed over a coupling lug and the recess at the end of the bar should be thrust against the diametrically-opposite lug.

(d) All suctions should be correctly secured by line in such a way that the line takes the full weight as follows.

Double the line into two equal halves and lay it alongside the suction hose with the centre of the line near to the strainer.

Place the running end of the line clear of operations.

Make a clove hitch around the neck of the strainer below the lugs.

If a basket strainer is fitted, the line should be adjusted over the skirt of the strainer in such a way as to catch the lugs.

Face the pump and place the right foot between the suction hose and the running part of the line. Coil the standing part of the line in the right hand.

Walk towards the pump with the suction hose between the feet. At each coupling lift the suction hose with the left hand and throw the coiled line underneath and around the suction hose to form a half hitch underneath the female coupling.

Tie off the line at the pump with a round turn and two half hitches. The tension of the line should be adjusted before the suction is lowered into the water so that each length is slightly bowed and the line takes the weight of the suction when in its final position.

The running end of the line should be taken from the strainer to the pump, to enable the strainer to be hauled up for cleaning.

(e) When refilling water tanks on appliances, pressure should not be allowed to build up after the tank is full; quite a small internal pressure is capable of doing substantial damage. Equally where a tank is fitted with an overflow, the continual outflow is not only wasteful but may cause flooding elsewhere, or where an appliance is standing on soft ground, cause it to become 'bogged down'.

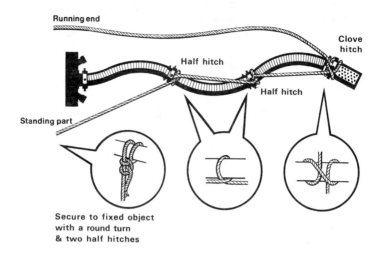

Running end

Clove hitch

Half hitch

Half hitch

Standing part

Secure to fixed object
with a round turn
& two half hitches

(f) Pumps should not be run without water in the casing longer than is necessary; this causes damage by wear on the impeller neck rings and, in some cases, to the pump gland.

(g) The drills set out in this section under the heading Pump Drills, apply equally to Water Tenders having a built in pump.

(h) At the completion of a drill, hose and equipment is generally made up and returned to the appliance by those who provided it. Additionally where more equipment than usual is laid out on either the delivery side or the inlet side of the pump, all members of a crew assist in making up regardless of whether or not they provided the equipment.

Drills may incorporate the changing from one set of equipment to another e.g. from the use of hose reel to main jet. For the purpose of the drill the disused equipment may be left until the general *'make up'* order is given. This would not be considered to be good practice on the fireground however. Equipment left lying around on the fireground should therefore be made up and restowed on the appliance as soon as circumstances allow.

Pump drills

See notes on hose drills page 24 and 'Notes on operation and use of pumps' page 34.

Getting the hose reel equipment to work (one hose reel) (Four men) — Drill P1

Preliminary detail: As given in PD3.

'Get to work'. The crew dismount No. 2 first engaging the pump and, moving at the double, No. 1 takes the hose reel and operates the reel valve where fitted, checking that the hose reel is charged by a short operation of the hose reel nozzle. No. 2 operates the tank valve. No. 1 takes the hose reel to the scene of the fire followed by Nos. 3 and 4 who clear the hose reel whilst No. 2 pulls it off the reel.

'To extend the hose-reel length when only one hose reel in use'. On the order *'Extend hose reel'* No. 4 returns to the appliance and assisted by No. 2 removes the branch and nozzle from the hose reel not in use and unreels sufficient tubing to form a large bight at the rear of the appliance.

No. 2 turns both hose reel valves to the 'off' position then disconnects the coupling of the original tubing from the reel-drum. The original tubing is then coupled to the new tubing and reel and the appropriate hose reel valve re-opened.

Whilst No. 2 opens the hose-reel valves to the new reel No. 4 reels off a quantity of tubing leaving a large bight at the appliance, in order to keep the hose reel clear of No. 2.

No. 4 then goes back to assist No. 1 and No. 3 straightening the hose as he goes.

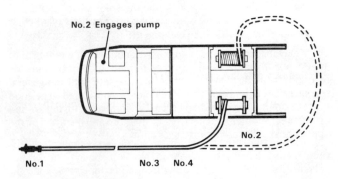

To augment the supply of water (or to refill the tank) from a hydrant. No. 4 takes a standpipe, hydrant key and bar, doubles to the hydrant, opens up the pit and ships the standpipe and hydrant key. No. 2 takes a length of hose, runs it out from the hydrant to the appliance and connects it to the tank inlet or collecting head. If

38

more than one length of soft suction is required, Nos 2 and 4 run out alternate lengths. No. 4 stands by the hydrant and turns on when ordered by No. 2. He then rejoins Nos 1 and 3 at the branch, assisting as necessary

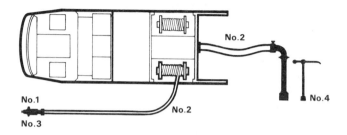

'Knock off' or 'Knock off and make up'. No. 1 sends back No. 4 with the message *'Knock off' or 'Knock off and make up'*. No. 2 will close the hose-reel valve where fitted.

'Make up' No. 2 disengages the pump and if the hydrant is at work, orders No. 4 to turn off the hydrant. No. 4 then makes up the suction side of the pump. Nos. 1, 2 and 3 make up the hose reel. The crew then mount, No. 1 reporting to the officer in charge.

Working from a hydrant using soft suction (one delivery) (Four men)   Drill P2

Preliminary detail. As given in PD3.

'Get to work'. The crew dismount, No. 2 first engaging the pump, and, moving at the double, No. 3 takes the first length of hose and runs it out from the pump. No. 1 takes a branch and a second length of hose and runs it out from the first length. No. 3 connects the first and second lengths of hose and No. 1 connects the branch. Meanwhile No. 2 removes the blank cap and connects the collecting head to the suction inlet (if it is not already connected), whilst No. 4 provides the standpipe, hydrant key and bar. No. 4 opens up the hydrant pit and ships the standpipe and key.

No. 2 takes a length of soft suction, runs it out from the hydrant to the pump and makes the connection. If more than one length of soft suction is required, Nos. 2 and 4 run out alternate lengths.

No. 4 doubles along the hose to the branch, straightening out any kinks and seeing that the hose is clear. When he arrives at the branch No. 1 sends back No. 4 with the message *'Water on'*, stating the number of the delivery, the pump pressure required and the position where the branch is at work, e.g. *'Water on No. 1 delivery, 3 bar pressure, branch working on the ground floor'*.

After giving the order to No. 2, No. 4 goes and turns on the hydrant at the order of No. 2, he then returns to the branch, repeats the message to No. 1 and generally assists as required.

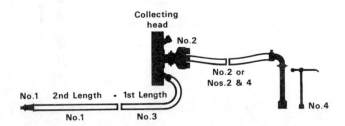

'Knock off' or **Knock off and make up'.** No. 1 sends back No. 4 with the message *'Knock off'* or *'Knock off and make up'.* No. 2 will shut down the delivery.

'Make up' No. 2 disengages the pump and orders No. 4 to shut down the hydrant, Nos. 2 and 4 make up the suction side of the pump. No. 1 returns the branch and Nos. 1 and 3 and, if necessary, No. 4 then underrun and make up the delivery hose.

The crew then mount, No. 1 reporting to the officer in charge.

Working from open water (one delivery) (Four men)

Drill P3

Preliminary detail. As given in PD3.

'Get to work'. The crew dismount No. 2 first engaging the pump and, moving at the double:

With one length of suction. No. 2 takes a suction wrench and removes the blank cap or collecting head. Nos. 2 and 4 take the length of suction with strainer and connect it to the pump. No. 2 tightens the joint.

With two lengths of suction. No. 2 provides two wrenches and removes the blank cap or collecting head. Nos. 1 and 3 take the first length of suction and connect it to the pump. Nos. 2 and 4 take the second length of suction with strainer connect it to the first length and tighten all joints.

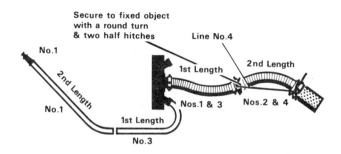

With three lengths of suction. No. 2 provides two wrenches and removes the blank cap or collecting head, Nos. 2 and 4 take the first length of suction and connect it to the pump. Nos. 1 and 3 take the second length of suction and connect it to the first. Nos. 2 and 4 take the third length of suction with strainer, connect it to the second length and tighten all joints.

No. 3 takes the first length of hose and runs it out from the pump. No. 1 takes the second length of hose and a branch and runs out the hose from the first length. No. 3 connects the first and second lengths of hose and then joins No. 1 at the branch. No. 1 connects the branch.

> *Note:* If only one length of hose is required, No. 3 will run it out. If more than two lengths are required, Nos. 3 and 1 will run out alternate lengths.

No. 4 takes a line and secures the suction and strainer (see page 36 para (d)), and, assisted by No. 2, places the suction into the water supply. No. 4 then doubles along the line of hose to the branch, straightening out any kinks and seeing that the hose is clear.

When No. 4 arrives at the branch, No. 1 sends No. 4 back with the message *'Water on'* stating the number of the delivery, the pump pressure required and the position where the branch is at work.

After giving the message to No. 2, No. 4 returns to the branch, repeats the message to No. 1 and then generally assists as required.

'**Knock off**' or **Knock off and make up**'. No. 1 sends No. 4 back to
No. 2 with the message '*Knock off*' or '*Knock off and make up*'.
No. 2 will close down the delivery.

'**Make up**' No. 2 disengages the pump.

No. 4 assists No. 2 to make up the suction side of the pump. No. 1
returns the branch and, assisted by No. 3 and, if necessary, No. 4
underruns and makes up all hose.
The crew then mount, No. 1 reporting to the officer in charge.

Getting the hose reel equipment to work (two hose reels) (Five men)

Drill P4

Preliminary detail. As given in PD4.

'**Get to work**'. The crew dismount, No. 2 first engaging the pump,
and moving at the double, Nos. 1 and 4 each takes a hose reel and
runs the hose to the scene of the fire.

Nos. 3 and 5 pull the hose reel hose off the respective reels and join
Nos. 1 and 4, clearing the hose as they go. No. 2 operates the hose
reel valves where fitted.

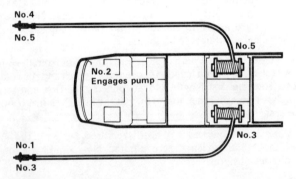

To augment the supply from a hydrant. As soon as the branches are
at work, No. 5 returns to the appliance, takes a standpipe, hydrant
key and bar, doubles to the hydrant, opens up the pit and ships the
standpipe and hydrant key.

No. 2 takes a length of hose, runs it out from the hydrant to the
appliance and connects it to the tank inlet or collecting head. If
more than one length of soft suction is required, Nos 2 and 5 run
out alternate lengths.

'Knock off' or 'Knock off and make up'. No. 1 sends back No.3 (and/or No. 4 sends back No. 5) with the message *'Knock off'* or *'Knock off and make up'.* No. 2 will close the hose reel valves (where fitted).

'Make up' No. 2 disengages the pump and, if the hydrant is at work, orders No. 5 to turn off the hydrant. Nos. 2 and 5 make up the suction side of the pump whilst Nos. 1, 3 and 4, make up the hose-reels.

The crew then mount, No. 1 reporting to the officer in charge.

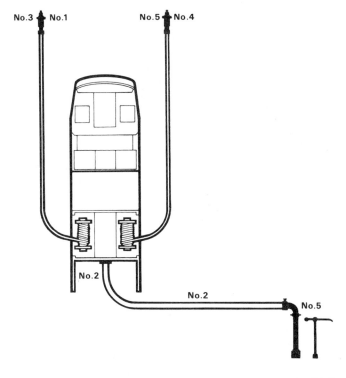

Working from a hydrant using soft suction (two deliveries) (Five men) **Drill P5**

Preliminary detail. As given in PD4.

'Get to work'. The crew dismount No. 2 first engaging the pump and moving at the double No. 5 takes a double-outlet standpipe where provided or a single-outlet standpipe and dividing breeching, hydrant key and bar, opens up the hydrant and ships the standpipe and key.

No. 2 takes a suction wrench, removes the blank cap and connects the collecting head to the suction inlet (if it is not already fitted). Nos. 4 and 5 each provide, and run out, one length of soft suction from the hydrant to the pump.

If more than one length of soft suction is required in each line, Nos. 1 and 3 will run out one line and Nos. 4 and 5 the other.

Meanwhile No. 3 takes a length of hose and runs it out from No. 1 Delivery. No. 1 takes a branch and a second length of hose and runs out the hose from the first length. No. 3 connects the first and second lengths of hose together and No. 1 connects the branch.

No. 5 takes a length of hose and runs it out from No. 2 Delivery. No. 4 takes a branch and a second length of hose and runs out this hose from the first length. No. 5 connects the first and second lengths of hose together and No. 4 connects the branch.

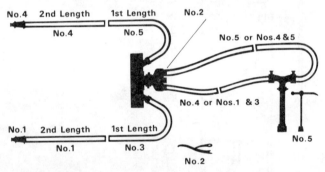

Note: If only one length of hose is required from each delivery, Nos. 3 and 5 will run them out. If more than two lengths are required Nos. 3 and 1 will run out alternate lengths from No. 1 Delivery and Nos. 5 and 4 will run out alternate lengths from No. 2 Delivery.

As soon as Nos. 1 and 4 are ready, they send back Nos. 3 and 5 respectively with the message *'Water on'*, stating the number of the delivery, the pump pressure required, and the positions where the branches are at work, the first man to arrive at the pump turns on the hydrant on the order of No. 2.

Nos. 3 and 5 then double back to their respective branches and repeat the message, seeing that the hose line is clear and free of kinks at the same time.

Note: No. 2 must open up his delivery valves and charge the hose slowly to allow a gradual build up of pressure so that the messengers can return to the branches and assist before the full flow is allowed to develop.

When two different pressures are ordered the pump must be operated at the lowest pressure.

'Knock off' or **'Knock off and make up'**. No. 1 sends back No. 3 (and/or No. 4 sends back No. 5) with the message *'Knock off No. 1 and/or No. 2 delivery'* or *'Knock off and make up'*. No. 2 will shut down the appropriate deliveries.

'Make up'. No. 2 disengages the pump and orders No. 5 to turn off the hydrant. Nos. 2 and 5 then make up the suction side of the pump. Nos. 1 and 4 return the branches and Nos. 1, 3 and 4 underrun and make up the delivery hose.
The crew then mount, No. 1 reporting to the officer in charge.

Note: Where the mains supply is low it may be necessary to get to work from two hydrants instead of one.

In this case Nos. 4 and 5 provide a standpipe hydrant key and bar and hose to work from the first hydrant. No. 5 ships the standpipe and both numbers run out the hose for connecting to the collecting head. No. 5 opens the hydrant on the order of No. 2. Nos. 4 and 5 then provide a second stand-pipe hydrant key and bar and the necessary hose and get to work from the second hydrant. When this is completed Nos. 4 and 5 run out the second line of delivery hose as detailed above.

No. 2 must control the speed of the pump to avoid overrunning the supply resulting in the flattening of the soft suction and uneven jets.

Working from open water (two deliveries) (Five men)

Drill P6

Preliminary detail. As given in PD4.

'Get to work'. The crew dismount No. 2 first engaging the pump and moving at the double:

With one length of suction. No. 2 takes a suction wrench and removes the blank cap or collecting head. Nos. 4 and 5 take a length of suction with strainer, connect it to the pump and tighten the joint.

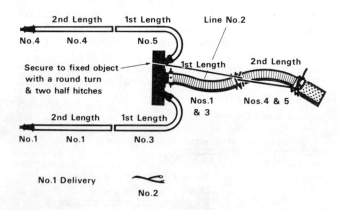

With two lengths of suction. No. 2 provides two suction wrenches and removes the blank cap or collecting head. Nos. 1 and 3 take the first length of suction and connect it to the pump. Nos. 4 and 5 take the second length of suction with strainer, connect it to the first and tighten all joints.

With three lengths of suction. The suctions are coupled as for two lengths, but Nos. 4 and 5 take the first and third lengths and Nos. 1 and 3 the second length.

No. 2 takes a line and secures the suction and strainer (see page 36 para d). Nos. 4 and 5 place the suction into the water supply.

The delivery hose is laid out as in Drill P5.

'Knock off' or **'Knock off and make up'**. No. 1 sends back No. 3 (and/or No. 4 sends back No.5) with the message *'knock off and make up'*. No. 2 will shut down the appropriate deliveries.

'Make up'. No. 2 disengages the pump, Nos. 2 and 5 make up the suction side of the pump.

Nos. 1 and 4 disconnect and return branches and Nos. 1, 3 and 4 underrun and make up all hose and replace gear.

The crew then mount, No. 1 reporting to the officer in charge.

Getting a ground monitor (or ancillary equipment) to work (Five men)   Drill P7

Preliminary detail. As given in PD4.

'Get to work'. The crew get to work and lay out the suction side of the pump as detailed in Drill P6 or, in the case of working from a hydrant or hydrants, using soft suction as detailed in Drill P5.

Nos. 1 and 3 double to the fire taking a ground monitor (or whichever ancillary equipment is to be used) together with a collecting breeching. Nos. 1 and 3 working from No. 1 Delivery and Nos. 4 and 5 working from No. 2 Delivery lay out the necessary number of lengths of hose and connect them to the breeching. The twin lines should be parallel and directly in line with the monitor for at least 3 metres before converging into the collecting breeching.

When all connections are made No. 1 sends back No. 5 with the message *'water on'*, Nos. 3 and 4 assist No. 1 as necessary.

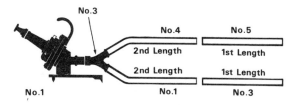

'Knock off' or **'Knock off and make up'**. No. 1 sends back No. 5 with the message *'Knock off' or 'Knock off and make up'*. No. 2 will shut down the deliveries.

'Make up'. No. 2 disengages the pump, Nos. 2 and 5 make up the suction side of the pump. Nos. 1 and 3 disconnect and return the collecting breeching and ground monitor, or ancillary equipment to the appliance. Nos. 1, 3, 4 and 5 underrun and make up all delivery hose and replace gear.

The crew then mount, No. 1 reporting to the officer in charge.

Note: When the ancillary equipment used is of excessive weight for Nos. 1 and 3, then Nos. 4 and 5 are to assist.

Water tender drills

See 'Notes on hose drills', page 24 and 'Notes on operation and use of pumps', page 34.

Getting the portable pump to work (Two deliveries) (Five men)

Drill WT1

Preliminary detail. As given in PD4.

'Get to work.' The crew dismount. Nos. 1, 2, 3 and 4 remove the portable pump from the appliance and, with No. 1 at the nearside front handle, No. 2 at the nearside rear, No. 3 at the offside rear and No. 4 at the offside front, the pump is carried to its working

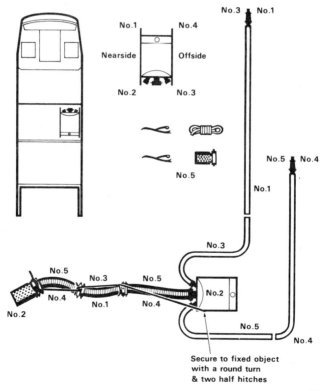

Secure to fixed object
with a round turn
& two half hitches

49

position. Meanwhile No. 5 provides suction wrenches, suction strainer and line. He then places them at the working position. The pump is then got to work as detailed in Drill P6.

> *Note:* If only one length of hose is required from each delivery Nos. 3 and 5 run them out. If more than two lengths are required, Nos. 3 and 1 run out alternate lengths from No. 1 Delivery and Nos. 5 and 4 run out alternate lengths from No. 2 Delivery.

As soon as Nos. 1 and 4 are ready, they send back Nos. 3 and 5 respectively with the message *'Water on, No. 1 (and/or No. 2) Delivery'*, stating the pressure required and the positions where the branches are at work. Nos. 3 and 5 then double back to their respective branches and repeat the message, at the same time straightening out any kinks and seeing that the hose is clear.

'Knock off' or **'Knock off and make up'.** No. 1 sends back No. 3 (and/or No. 4 sends back No. 5) with the message *'Knock off No. 1 Delivery (and/or No. 2 delivery)* or *Knock off and make up'*. No. 2 will shut down the appropriate deliveries.

'Make up'. Nos. 2 and 5 make up the suction side of the pump. Nos. 1 and 4 disconnect and return branches and Nos. 1, 3 and 4 underrun and make up all hose and replace gear. Nos. 1, 2, 3 and 4 replace the portable pump on the appliance.

The crew then mount, No. 1 reporting to the officer in charge.

Tables of main work for crews

In order that the detail of getting to work for pump drills may be more easily remembered, the main work to be carried out by each member of the crew for the greater number of drills is outlined broadly in Table 1.

In all pump drills No. 2 of the crew is always the pump operator; he also generally prepares the pump inlet fittings and, assisted by No. 4 and/or No. 5, normally provides the equipment to supply the pump with water. Nos. 1 and 3 provide the delivery equipment for the first line of hose, and also assist with additional equipment for the inlet side of the pump as necessary. Nos. 4 and 5 provide equipment for a second delivery line when required.

Table 1 Pump and Water Tender drills

	Drill	Pump operator	Standpipe, hydrant key and bar	Blank cap, collecting head, suction adaptor	Soft suction	Hard suction
P1	One hose reel, hydrant soft suction (4 men)	2	4		2 & 4	
P2	One delivery, hydrant, soft suction (4 men)	2	4	2	2 & 4	
P3	One delivery, open water (4 men)	2		2		*1 & 3 2 & 4
P4	Two hose reels, hydrant soft suction (5 men)	2	5		2 & 5	
P5	Two deliveries, hydrant(s), soft suction (5 men)	2	5 (or 4 & 5)	2	4 & 5 (or 1 & 3/4&5)	
P6	Two deliveries, open water (5 men)	2		2		1 & 3 4 & 5
P7	Two deliveries, ground monitor or ancillary equipment, open water (5 men)	2		2	As P5 or P6	
WT1	Two deliveries, open water portable pump 5 men	2		2		1 & 3 4 & 5

* Where four lengths of suction are used, Nos. 1 and 3, and 2 and 4 will take alternate lengths.

At the completion of a drill, hose and equipment is generally made up and returned to the appliance by those who provided it. Additionally where more equipment than usual is laid out on either the delivery side or the inlet side of the pump, all members of a crew assist in making up regardless of whether or not they provided the equipment.

It may be that a drill may incorporate the changing from one set of equipment to another e.g. from the use of hose reel to main jet. For the purpose of the drill the disused equipment may be left until the general *'make up'* order is given. This would not be considered to be good practice on the fireground however, Equipment left lying around on the fireground should therefore be made up and restowed on the appliance as soon as circumstances allow.

Connect suctions	Tighten suctions	Suction strainer and basket	Fix line to suction	Hose reel or delivery line 1	Hose reel or delivery line 2	Branch	Ground monitor or other ancillary equipment	Breeching, hose etc.
				1 & 3				
				1 & 3		1		
2 & 4	2 or 2 & 4	4	4	1 & 3		1		
				1 & 3	4 & 5			
				1 & 3	4 & 5	1 & 4		
4 & 5	4 & 5	2	2	1 & 3	4 & 5	1 & 4		
4 & 5	4 & 5	2	2	1 & 3	4 & 5		1 & 3	1 & 3
4 & 5	4 & 5	2	2	1 & 3	4 & 5	1 & 4		

Foam Drills

Notes on foam drills

1. Safety

(a) The man in control of the branch should direct it away from the fire until foam has started to flow in the place of water.

(b) Foam branches/pipes should be positioned so that foam may be poured in a continuous blanket over the surface of burning liquids.

(c) Any residual concentrate in a canister or tin which has been opened should be used only for drill purposes and should be marked accordingly.

(d) When more than one foam making branch is working from a pump operating a round-the-pump proportioner it is essential that the line of delivery from the pump outlet containing the delivery inset adaptor is not closed down whilst other foam branches are being supplied from the same pump.

2. General

(a) When a drill has been completed, all hose and equipment should be flushed with fresh water before being restowed. Particular attention should be paid to the filters and strainers in *all* foam equipment.

(b) The basic drills are to be adapted, where appropriate, in order to perform drills with other foam producing equipment. The extended use of foam branchpipes requires a continuous unbroken supply of foam concentrate. This will need more than just one or two members of a crew and, in the case of multiple branches, a whole crew may be required to maintain the supply.

Foam Drills

See "Notes on hose-drills" page 24, 'Notes on operation and use of pumps" page 34 and "Notes on foam drills" above.

Foam making branchpipe with pick-up tube (four men)

Drill F1

Preliminary detail. As given in PD3

'Get to work'. The suction side of the pump is got to work as detailed in Drills P2 or P3.

No.1 provides the foam making branchpipe and pick-up tube, and doubles to the fire.

No.3 takes a length of hose, connects it to the pump delivery and runs it out towards the fire, he then takes a container of foam concentrate to the foam branchpipe, connects the pick up tube and inserts it into the foam container.

No.1 takes a second length of hose, runs it out from the first length and connects it to the foam branchpipe.

No.4 doubles to the foam branchpipe along the line of hose straightening out any kinks and seeing that the hose is clear, and, when ready, is sent back by No.1 with the message 'Water on'. After giving the message to No. 2, No. 4 goes to the hydrant and turns on at the order of No. 2.

No.4 then returns to the branch with additional foam concentrate and assists as necessary by providing further concentrate and carrying messages.

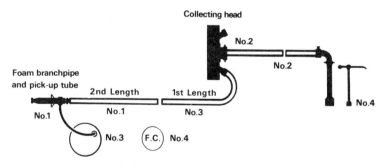

'Knock off' or **'Knock off' and 'make up'.** No.1 sends back No.4 with the message *'Knock off' or 'Knock off' and 'make up'.* No. 2 will shut down the delivery.

'Make up'.

No. 2 disengages the pump and orders No. 4 to shut down the hydrant. As soon as the flow ceases, Nos.1 and 3 return the branchpipe, pick-up tube and foam concentrate containers. Nos. 2 and 4 make up the suction side of the pump and all numbers underrun and make up hose as necessary.

The crew then mount, No.1 reporting to the officer in charge.

Preliminary detail. As given in PD4.

'Get to work'. The suction side of the pump is got to work as detailed in Drills P5 or P6.

No.1 provides the generator and pick up tube and places it on the ground close to the pump. No. 3 takes a length of hose (usually a special short length), connects it to the pump and then to the generator. No. 3 then takes a length of hose, connects it to the generator and runs it out in the direction of the fire. No. 1 returns to the pump, takes a length of hose and a foam branch, connects the hose to No. 3's length and runs it out. No. 1 connects the branch and No. 3 joins him. Nos. 4 and 5 provide the foam dam and foam concentrate and connect the pick-up tub and insert it in the foam dam and maintain a supply of foam concentrate.

When No. 1 is ready he sends back No. 3 with the message 'Water on'. No. 3 gives the message to No. 4 before giving it to No. 2 and then returns to the branch. No. 2 opens the pump delivery and increases the pressure to 10 bar.

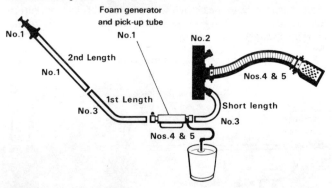

'Knock off' or **'Knock off' and 'make up'**. No. 1 sends back No. 3 with the message *'Knock off' or 'Knock off' and 'make up'*. No. 2 will shut down the delivery.

'Make up'.

No. 2 disengages the pump.

As soon as the flow ceases, No. 1 disconnects and returns the branch. No. 4 disconnects the generator and, assisted by No. 5, returns the generator, pick-up tube, foam dam and foam concentrate containers. No. 5 assists No. 2 to make up the suction side of the pump, and Nos. 1, 3 and 4 underrun and make up hose. The crew then mount, No. 1 reporting to the officer in charge.

Preliminary detail. As given in PD4

'Get to work'. The suction side of the pump is got to work as detailed in Drills P5 or P6.

No. 1 provides the generator, pick up tube and breeching, places the generator in position close to the pump and connects the breeching to the generator outlet.

No. 3 takes a length of hose (usually a special short length) connects it to the pump and then to the generator.

He then takes a length of hose, connects it to an outlet from the breeching, and runs it out in the direction of the fire.

No. 1 takes a length of hose and a foam branch, connects the hose to No. 3's length, runs it out and connects the branchpipe. No. 3 joins No. 1 at the branch.

Nos. 4 and 5 provide the foam dam and foam concentrate connect up the pick-up tube and insert it into the foam dam.

No. 5 then takes a length of hose, connects it to the other outlet from the breeching, and runs it out towards the fire. No. 4 takes a length of hose and a foam branch, connects the hose to No. 5's length, runs it out and connects the branch.

When all is ready No. 1 sends back No. 3 with the message 'Water on', No. 3 returns to the branches assisting as required. No. 2 opens the pump delivery and increases the pressure to 10 bar. No. 5 maintains the supply of foam concentrate.

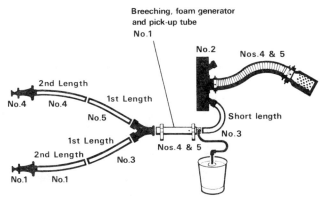

'Knock off' or **'Knock off' and 'make up'**. No. 1 sends back No. 3 with the message *'Knock off' or 'Knock off and make up'*. No. 2 will shut down the delivery.

'Make up'.

No. 2 disengages the pump.

As soon as the flow ceases, Nos. 1 and 4 disconnect and return the branches. No. 3 disconnects the generator and assisted by No. 5 returns the generator, breeching, pick-up tube, foam dam and foam concentrate containers. No. 5 assists No. 2 to make up the suction side of the pump. Nos. 1, 3 and 4 underrun and make up the hose.

The crew then mount, No. 1 reporting to the officer in charge.

Variable Inductor and No. 10   Drill F4
Foam Branchpipe (Five men)

Preliminary detail. As given in PD4.

'Get to work'. The crew dismount. No. 2 removes the blank cap or collecting head, and connects the suction adaptor and variable inductor to the pump inlet (unless the inductor is built in). The suction side of the pump is then got to work as detailed in Drill P5 or P6. When getting to work from a hydrant a pressure control valve should be fitted on the suction side of the inductor.

No.1 connects the delivery adaptor to the pump, provides the pick-up tube and inductor hose, and connects them to the variable inductor. No. 3 takes a length of hose, runs it out from the delivery adaptor towards the fire.

No. 1 takes a second length of hose and a foam making branchpipe, connects it to the first length, runs it out, connects the branchpipe and when ready sends back No. 3 with the message 'Water on'. No. 3 returns to the branchpipe No. 2 operates the inductor control, as appropriate.

Nos. 4 and 5 provide the foam dam and foam concentrate, insert the pick-up tube in the foam dam, and maintain the supply of foam concentrate.

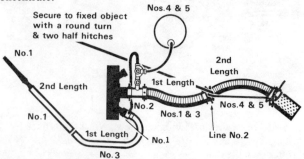

'Knock off' or **'Knock off'** and **'make up.'** No. 1 sends back No. 3 with the message *'Knock off' or 'Knock off' and 'make up'.* No. 2 will shut down the delivery.

58

'Make up'.

No. 2 disengages the pump.
As soon as the flow ceases, No. 1 disconnects and returns the foam branchpipe. Nos. 2 and 5 make up the suction side of the pump and, assisted by No. 4, return foam equipment and concentrate containers. Nos. 1 and 3 underrun and make up the hose.
The crew then mount, No. 1 reporting to the officer in charge.

Tables of main work for crews

In order that the detail of getting to work for foam drills may be more easily remembered, the main work to be carried out by each member of the crew for the greater number of drills is outlined broadly in Table II.

In all foam drills the suction side of the pump is got to work in the same way as for the pump drills, according to the number of men available and the type of water supply. As with pump drills Nos. 1 and 3 generally provide equipment on the delivery side of the pump, while the higher numbers usually provide inductors and maintain supplies of foam concentrate.

Table II Foam drills

	Drill	Suction side, as in pump drill No:	Delivery line 1
F1	Foam branchpipe, pick-up tube (4 men)	P2, or 3	1 & 3
F2	Foam generator (FG 5A) (5 men)	P5 or 6	1 & 3
F3	Foam generator (FG 10) (5 men)	P5 or 6	1 & 3
F4	Variable inductor	P5 or 6	1 & 3

* See note 2(b) on page 53

At the completion of a drill, hose and equipment is generally made up and returned to the appliance by those who provided it. Additionally where more equipment than usual is laid out on either the delivery side or the inlet side of the pump, all members of a crew assist in making up regardless of whether or not they provided the equipment.

The provision of foam concentrate by No. 4 or Nos. 4 and 5 represents a purely token situation. The extended use of foam branchpipes requires a continued unbroken supply of foam concentrate and involves more than one or two members of a crew to maintain it.

Delivery line 2	Foam branch-pipe	Pick-up tubes	Foam dam tank or container	Generator or inductor	Adaptors	Foam con-centrate*
	1	1	3			3 & 4
	1	1	4 & 5	1		4 & 5
4 & 5	1 & 4	1	4 & 5	1		4 & 5
	1	4	4 & 5	2	1 & 3	4 & 5

Escape and extension ladder drills

Notes on Escape and Extension Ladder Drills

Safety

The following points must be adhered to in order to ensure maximum safety when operating with wheeled escapes or extension ladders. Any reference to ladders includes the ladders of wheeled escapes.

1.   Helmets must be worn by all personnel.

2.   A ladder should, as far as circumstances permit, be pitched to the right hand side of a window or other opening with, where possible, three rounds above the sill.

3.   When a ladder is pitched and extended the pawls must be properly engaged with the rounds in line and the heel correctly footed or manned before any attempt is made to climb or descend.

4.   Chocks should be placed under the outside of the wheel, using the outer hand, the inner hand resting on and exerting a pressure against the carriage frame. The rear chock should be placed in position (again with the outer hand) whilst working from the back of the escape with the inner hand on the escape axle. The chocks should be tapped securely into place with the foot.

5.   When extending or lowering an escape which is not fitted with a friction brake, particular care must be taken to ensure that control is kept of the winch handles. Care must also be taken with certain types of friction brake, the performance of which may be adversely affected by water. When using the extending or carriage gear, the winch handles should be grasped with both hands, whether or not a friction brake is fitted.

6.   When manoeuvring an escape, the *spokes* of the wheels must be used by the men manning the wheels. The hands must not be placed on the wheel rims.

7.   When climbing or descending a ladder the arms should be kept reasonably straight, thus forcing the body well away from the ladder, the hands should grasp the rounds with thumbs on the underside. The strings should only be grasped when a ladder is bridged at a low angle, or whilst using the cradle-carry rescue technique.

8.   When stepping off a ladder personnel should ascend to the level of, or to the round above, the parapet or window sill before stepping off with the outside foot, i.e. with the left foot if to the left, or with the right foot if to the right.

9.   When getting out of a window or from a parapet and stepping up on to a ladder pitched to the right, the head iron or a convenient round should be grasped from the rear underside with the left hand palm uppermost. The right foot should be placed on the round above the sill or parapet; at the same time the top of a round should be grasped with the right hand until the left hand has been moved and is grasping a convenient round (from the front). At no time should both hands be off the escape or ladder and never should a step down be made on to a ladder except as outlined in para. 11 below.

10.   When moving from one ladder to another, either climbing or descending, the nearest foot must always be placed on the ladder first, then the nearest hand, followed by the other hand and then the other foot.

11.   It may not always be possible to stand on a window sill to commence a carry down, either because the height of the window opening is insufficient or because there are no convenient objects such as steps available to assist, and in these circumstances the straddle method should be used, as follows:

The body should be placed across the shoulders in the normal manner for carrying down. A convenient round of the ladder should be grasped from the underside with the hand palm uppermost. Placing one leg over the sill, the straddle position should be taken up, facing and close to the ladder string.

The outer foot should then be placed on a convenient round just below the window sill and a convenient round above the sill should be continuously grasped with the outer hand.

Manoeuvring as close to the ladder as possible, the outer foot should be transferred to a convenient lower round, the position of the outer foot should be as far across the ladder as possible adjacent to the furthermost string. The weight should be transferred to the outer foot at the same time pulling up on the ladder, then the inner hand and foot should be transferred on to the ladder.

Both hands should be on one round and both feet on a lower round before the descent is commenced.

12. When ascending or descending, particularly in carrying down, hands and feet should be moved in unison, i.e. right hand, right foot, left hand, left foot, and so on (Plate 11).

13. When carrying a person/dummy down an escape ladder with the head over the left shoulder, the man carrying should step off to the right clear of the escape and then turn left about. This will prevent the head of the person/dummy being carried from striking the carriage wheel.

14. The carriage gear must be used if a safe working angle cannot be obtained by manoeuvering the head of the escape into the building. The head must be rested on the building, and the weight of the ladder taken on the carriage wheels and the lever wheels. On no account must the escape be pitched so that the weight of the ladder is taken off the carriage or the lever wheels. The only time the latter should be allowed to rise from the ground is when it is necessary to bridge an escape (Drill E5) under which circumstance the largest number of men available should man the levers.

15. When lowering a dummy on a short extension ladder or on a stretcher, by means of a line from an escape (Drill E4), a guy line must always be used. The guy line should be attached to the centre of the stretcher or ladder.

16.   As the overlap of extensions is reached during the descent, the warning *'step in'* or *'step out'* should be given, according to the type of ladder.

17.   On descent when the feet are one round above the pawls the warning *'pawls'* should be given.

18.   As the lowest round of an escape is reached the warning *'heel-board'* should be given.

19.   During carrying down, men on the escape should be guided clear of any guy lines, and where quick release guy wires are fitted these should be disconnected and reconnected prior to making up.

20.   When working on a ladder and it is necessary to use both hands a leg lock should always be taken particularly prior to *'Water on'* being ordered when working with a branch.

21.   There are two methods by, which an escape may be secured on the headrest of an appliance:

(i)   by head-locking gear operated manually by a lever in the crew's cab, (as with 'trunnion' and 'Miles' mountings), and

(ii) by brackets on the strings of the main ladder which automatically engage with the headrest, (as with a *'push-in'* mounting), in which case a manual-locking device is incorporated in the rear mountings to lock the escape in the forward position.

These two methods of mounting require slight variations in the drills, and details of the drills for slipping an escape and for replacing an escape on an appliance are therefore set out under two headings:

(i)   *trunnion and Miles mountings*, and

(ii) *push-in mountings*.

22.   The officer in charge of ladder drills is required to judge if special precautions are necessary due to weather conditions.

23.   Where an escape line is fitted care should be taken to ensure that it is laid between the strings and does not interfere with the head-locking gear or brackets on the strings.

24. **To lift and carry a 10.5m ladder with not less than two men.**
No.1 on the nearside at the head makes ready to grasp the string farther away from him while No. 2 on the offside at the heel grasps the string nearer to him and lifts the ladder so that No. 1 can get his hand around the string. The ladder should be carried by the upper string with the rounds vertical. If there are three men. Nos. 1 and 2 grasp the head and No. 3 the heel of both strings and the ladder is carried with the rounds horizontal.

25. **To lift and cary a 13.5m ladder with not less than four men.**
Nos. 1 and 2 grasp the head and Nos. 3 and 4 the heel of the ladder and carry it with the rounds horizontal.

26. Before placing the heel of an extension ladder on the ground, prior to under-running, ensure that the correct side of the ladder is uppermost and the ladder heel is firmly postioned. It is essential that both men remain in close contact until they have completed under-running particularly when handling the heavier 13.5m ladder.

27. When a ladder is pitched the ideal distance of the heel of the ladder from the base of the building is approximately one-third of the working height of the ladder (one quarter of working height for standard testing).

28. Before an extension ladder is extended it should be stable with the heel of each string or the jack pads steady on the ground.

29. While a ladder is being extended or housed (3 men) each string should be steadied with the hand nearer the building reaching up and with the hand away from the building reaching down. The foot farther from the building should be placed at the heel of the ladder (Plate 8). Feet must never be placed on the rounds when extending or lowering.

30. Extension ladders must always be held in such a manner that fingers will not be trapped by the extending sections and fingers kept outside the strings, away from mounting guide brackets. When handles are fitted for this purpose, they should be used.

31. When an extension ladder is being extended the line must be pulled in as nearly a vertical position as possible, with the hands as close to the ladder as the rounds permit.

32. When an extension ladder is being extended any tendency of the pull on the extending line to cause the ladder to tilt should be resisted, but a ladder should always be slightly inclined towards the

building while it is being extended, and should never be allowed to lean away from the building.

If at any time an officer in charge of a drill considers that the crew are losing control he should order *'Head in'*. Each member of the crew should then strive to place the head of the ladder against the building to obtain some measure of stability.

33.   When an extension ladder has been extended, manual pawls must be tripped by placing the arm round the string and not through the ladder.

34.   When an extension ladder is being housed the extending line must be paid out hand under hand, and must not be allowed to slide through the palms of the hand.

35.   When an extension ladder is housed the pawls should rest on the bottom or second round as appropriate.

36.   The head of an extension ladder should only be secured when necessary, e.g. in high winds or when it is certain that a ladder will not be required elsewhere. In a drill yard surounded by buildings, care should be taken to assess the effects of the wind upon the head of the ladder when it is raised above roof level.

37.   When one man has to *'foot'* an extension ladder he should place his right foot on the lowest round, brace his left leg well back, grasp both strings, and press on the ladder (Plate 9). Where two men are available each man should place his inner foot on the lowest round, brace his outer foot well back, grasp a string and press on the ladder (Plate 10).

38.   Additional notes on 13.5m extension ladder drills

(a)   When footing, the jack beam is to be considered as the bottom round of the ladder. However when the extensions are not resting on the pawls (i.e. when extending or lowering) the ladder should be footed by the straddle method with the feet resting on the jack beam outside the strings of the main ladder. Exceptionally the outside feet are used when lowering the head of the ladder into the building (see Drill L3).

(b)   When a 13.5m ladder is being underrun, the maximum thrust or pull should be exerted at the head when the props are in line with the strings.

(c)   Plumbing should be carried out after the ladder has been under-run and before it is extended. Final adjustments may be made after the ladder has been extended, and the head is resting on the building.

(d) When the ladder is pitched and ready for work, the jacks should be in such a position that the full weight of the ladder is on the jacks.

(e) During extending and housing it is essential that weight is evenly maintained on the jacks.

(f) If necessary the ladder can be raised against a building and extended by allowing the head wheels to run up the wall; the heel of the ladder can then be moved to a safe working angle when the required height has been reached.

(g) Normally the 13.5m ladder should be climbed at a steady pace. On occasions when rapid climbing is required or unstable conditions prevail the props should be manned to control and restrain excessive movement of the ladder After each ascent or descent the position of the props should be checked to ensure that the ladder remains stable.

39. Additional Notes on Bridging Ladders

(a) There should be not less than 650mm of ladder on each side of the gap being bridged.

(b) When bridging an escape: the ladders should be fully lowered out in the carriage with the heel chain at maximum length and/or the carriage stops securely engaged.

(c) when extended the projection beyond the carriage wheels of an escape to the head of the ladder should not exceed 9.3m.

(d) The largest number of men available should man the levers.

(e) Except in an emergency not more than two men should be allowed on the bridged portion of an escape.

(f) When bridging a 10.5m ladder the overall length, when extended, should not exceed 8m, and the gap to be bridged should not exceed 6m. Except in an emergency not more than one man should be allowed on the bridged portion of the ladder. Care should be taken to avoid undue oscillation when moving across the bridged ladder.

(g) Officers, who are in charge of a bridging drill, should consider the use of safety lines, particularly, for example over water, and personnel must be made aware of the danger of losing balance when crossing a bridged ladder.

(h) It is common practice to permanently mark the strings of the main ladder to indicate the maximum permissible extension for bridging.

Notes on the use of Roof Ladders

Whilst it is not possible to cater for all the circumstances in which roof ladders may be used, the following points of guidance should be observed wherever practicable.

1. An extension ladder should be pitched to a point slightly to one side of the position that a roof ladder is to be used. The ladder should be extended, preferably, about 5 rounds above the eaves, to enable a leg lock to be taken above eaves level. Extra care should be taken when ladders are resting on plastic guttering. (The weight of a laden ladder could cause damage to or flexing of the guttering resulting in the ladder becoming unstable).

2. The roof ladder should be underrun, hook uppermost, and positioned adjacent to the strings of the extension ladder on the side that it is to be used with the hook pointing towards the opposite string. One man should mount the extension ladder and ascend until he is able to place one arm between the fourth and fifth round of the roof ladder with the round resting firmly on his shoulder. The man should then continue to ascend to a point above the eaves when a leg lock can be taken with the leg opposite to the side that the roof ladder is being carried.

3. The roof ladder should be transferred from the shoulder and, grasping both strings with the wheels resting on the roof, manoeuvred towards the ridge at an angle of approximately 10 degrees away from the extension ladder. Once the hook has passed beyond the ridge the roof ladder should be turned over, towards the extension ladder, and adjusted to ensure that the hook is resting firmly on the opposite side of the roof.

4. When transferring to or from the roof ladder the sequence of movements must be foot, hand, hand, foot, the nearest foot/hand being transferred first.

5. When making up the roof ladder the reverse procedure must be adopted, one crew member receiving the roof ladder when the man on the extension ladder approaches the ground. The roof ladder should be underrun and carried clear of operations.

Escape drills

Slipping the escape (Four men)   Drill E1

Preliminary detail. As given in PD3.

(i) *With 'Trunnion' and 'Miles' mountings:*

No. 1 gives the order *'Stand by to slip'*. Nos. 1, 2 and 3 dismount and double towards the rear of the appliance, No. 1 taking up a position at the nearside carriage wheel, Nos. 2 and 3 standing about one pace clear of the levers at the rear of the appliance, No. 2 on the offside and No. 3 on the nearside. (Nos. 2 and 3 must keep their legs clear of the levers as the escape is lowered.)

As soon as No. 1 is satisfied that all is in readiness for the escape to be slipped, he gives the order *'Slip'*, No. 4 releases the head-securing gear and calls out *'released'*, Nos. 2 and 3 pull down on the levers and lower the escape to the ground (taking care that when the counterbalance position is reached the weight is taken up to prevent the escape from striking the ground too heavily).

No. 4 dismounts and as soon as the escape is on the ground, No. 2 moves to the offside carriage wheel, and No. 4 moves into the position on the offside of the levers vacated by No. 2.

(ii) *With 'push-in' mountings:*

No. 1 gives the order *'Stand by to slip'*. The crew dismount and double towards the rear of the appliance, No. 1 taking up a position at the nearside carriage wheel, No. 2 at the offside wheel, Nos. 3 and 4 standing about one pace clear of the levers at the rear of the appliance, No. 3 on the nearside, No. 4 on the offside. (Nos. 3 and 4 should take care to keep their legs clear of the levers as the escape is lowered).

As soon as No. 1 is satisfied that all is in readiness for the escape to be slipped, he gives the order *'Slip'*. The appropriate member (or members) of the crew release the securing gear and calls out *'released'*, all members pull the escape backwards on the slides before Nos. 3 and 4 apply their weight downwards to lower the escape to the ground, (taking care that when the counterbalance position is reached, the weight is taken up to prevent the escape from striking the ground too heavily).

Note: If an escape is to be left slipped and unused, No. 1 puts down the wheel chocks on the nearside and No. 2 on the offside. The wheel chocks are to be placed fore and aft of each wheel and the ladders let out fully in the carriage if the head is not resting.

'Make up'

(i) *With 'Trunnion' and 'Miles' mountings:*

No. 1 takes up a position at the nearside carriage wheel, No. 2 at the offside carriage wheel, and Nos. 3 and 4 at the levers. The crew manoeuvre the escape into position, Nos. 1 and 2 ensure that the ladders are plumbed central and Nos. 3 and 4 guide Nos. 1 and 2 to ensure that the escape is correctly aligned with the mounting on the appliance.

When No. 1 sees all is in readiness he gives the order *'Counterbalance'*. With Nos. 1 and 2 pulling forward on the carriage wheels, Nos. 3 and 4 lift the levers; as soon as the escape engages with the appliance mountings Nos. 1 and 2 move to assist Nos. 3 and 4, when the carriage wheels are clear of the ground Nos. 1, 2, 3 and 4 then lower the head of the escape gently on to the headrest, No. 4 then locks the securing gear. When No. 1 has made a physical check that the escape locking hooks have fully engaged over the trunnion bar and that the gravity hook (where fitted) has engaged the top extension and the escape line (where fitted) is clear of the head securing gear, he calls *'Secured'*. Nos. 2 and 3 then apply their weight to the heel to ensure that the securing gear is holding the escape in position on the appliance.

The crew then mount, No. 1 reporting to the officer in charge.

(ii) *With 'push-in' mountings:*

No. 1 takes up a position at the nearside carriage wheel, No. 2 at the offside carriage wheel, and Nos. 3 and 4 at the levers. The crew manoeuvre the escape into position, Nos. 3 and 4 direct the operation to ensure that the escape is correctly aligned with the mountings on the appliance. Nos. 1 and 2 ensure that the ladders are plumbed to the central position.

When No. 1 sees all is in readiness, he gives the order *'Counterbalance'*. With Nos. 1 and 2 pulling forward on the carriage wheels, Nos. 3 and 4 lower the head of the escape gently on to the headrest. When the escape has been lowered on to the headrest No. 1 gives the order *'Launch'*, Nos. 1 and 2, assisted by 3 and 4 at the heel then push the escape forward on the carriage frame until the securing gear locks.

When No. 1 has ensured that the head and rear fastenings are secure, he checks any visual warning and calls *'Secured'*. Nos. 3 and 4 then apply their weight to the heel to ensure that the securing gear is holding the escape in position on the appliance.

The crew then mount, No. 1 reporting to the officer in charge.

Pitching the escape and effecting a rescue by carrying down (Four men)　　　　　　**Drill E2**

Preliminary detail. As given in PD3.

'Get to work'. The escape is slipped as detailed in Drill E1.

With No. 1 on the nearside wheel, No. 2 on the offside wheel and Nos. 3 and 4 on the levers, the escape is manhandled into the required position for extending. If plumbing gear is fitted and it is necessary to use it, No. 1 or 2 will operate it according to the position of the control, No. 4 giving the order *'Well'*, when the escape is vertical. When in position, Nos. 1 and 2 extend the ladders to the required height, No. 4 giving the order *'Well'*.

If necessary all four members of the crew should manoeuvre the head of the escape into position. If the carriage gear is to be used, Nos. 1 and 2 put down the wheel chocks and then man the carriage gear and lower out into the carriage. Because during the actual carry the weight of 'two men' will be applied to the ladder, care should be taken to operate at as steep an angle as practicable.

Nos. 1 and 2 man the levers, whilst No. 3, followed by No. 4, mounts the escape and enters the building, No. 4 taking the escape line into the building with him. No. 3 then effects the rescue by carrying down.

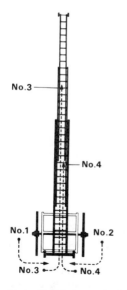

'Make up'. Nos. 1 and 2 wind the escape up in the carriage to the 'mount' points. Nos. 1 and 2 then move to the extending gear, house the ladders, remove the wheel chocks, and centralise the plumbing if necessary.

With No. 1 on the nearside wheel, No. 2 on the offside wheel, and Nos. 3 and 4 on the levers, the crew then manoeuvre the escape into position for mounting it on to the appliance.

The escape is then placed on the appliance as detailed in Drill E1.

Note: If only two winch handles are carried on the escape, one will be kept on the extending gear on the nearside and one on the carriage gear on the offside. No. 2 will then be responsible for raising or lowering the escape in the carriage. He will, however, move his winch handle to the extending gear to assist No. 1 in extending or housing the ladders, if necessary.

Getting a line of hose to work up an escape (Four men)

Drill E3

Preliminary detail. As detailed in PD3.

'Get to work'. The escape is slipped, pitched and extended as detailed in drills E1 and E2. The pump is got to work as detailed in Drills P2 or P3. No. 1 provides a length of hose and a branch and runs out the hose in a long bight at the foot of the escape. No. 3 provides a hose becket or sling and a length of hose which he runs out from the pump to the foot of the escape laying it ready for connection by No. 4 on the order *'Water on'*.

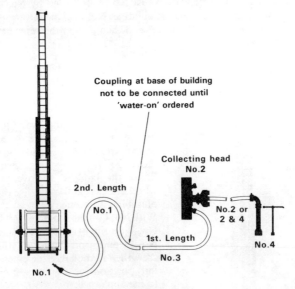

Coupling at base of building
not to be connected until
'water-on' ordered

Collecting head
No.2

2nd. Length

No.1

No.2 or
2 & 4

1st. Length

No.4

No.3

No.1

When the levers are manned by No. 3 No. 1 passes the hose under his arm and over his shoulder, the branch hanging down to the rear to a point in the centre of his back, mounts the escape, and enters the building No. 3 lightening the hose.

No. 3 when the levers are manned by No. 4, mounts the escape, takes a leg-lock, secures the hose becket or sling to the hose and to the round of the escape below the sill and follows No. 1 into the building. No. 4 lightens the hose over the levers and sees that it lies on the escape.

Note: No. 4 must be in a position at the levers whilst Nos. 1 and or 3 are mounting or descending the escape.

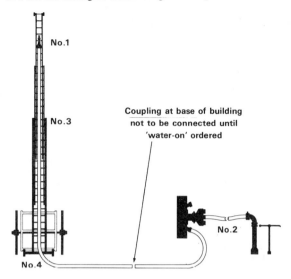

When all is in readiness No. 1 sends back the message *'Water on'* (by way of Nos. 3 and 4) stating the number of the delivery, the pump pressure required and the position of the branch. The coupling at the foot of the escape is connected by No. 4 before he makes his way to No. 2 with the order *'Water on'*. No. 4 then returns to the heel of the escape.

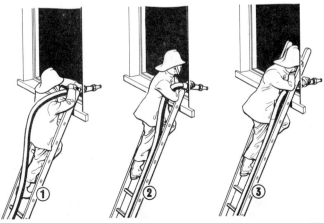

Note: If the branch is got to work from the head of the ladder the hose becket or sling should be attached to a more convenient round. No. 3 should, after securing the hose, descend to man the levers if No. 4 has to leave the heel to pass on the message *'Water on'* or *'Knock off'*.

Correct method of branch holding at the head of a ladder

Method 1. The face can be kept at sill level and is thus protected from the heat and smoke escaping from the window.

Method 2. When the ladder is pitched to, but not above, the sill, the branch being held very much as on the ground.

Method 3. When the ladder projects several rounds above the sill.

'Knock off and make up'. No. 1 sends back No. 4 to No. 2 with the message *'Knock off'* or *'Knock off and make up'*. No. 2 will close down the delivery.

'Make up'. No. 2 will release the pressure and disengage the pump. No. 4 then returns to the foot of the escape and breaks the hose coupling nearest to it before manning the levers.

No. 3 then mounts the escape, takes a leg lock, removes the hose becket or sling and takes the hose from No. 1, placing it over his shoulder, branch to the rear. No. 3 descends the escape followed by No. 1, No. 4 taking in the slack hose as it comes down.

All gear is then made up as detailed in:

Drill P2 or P3 for the pump.
Drills E1 and E2 for the escape.

Notes:

1. This drill can also be carried out using an extension ladder, the ladder being pitched as detailed in Drills L1, L2, L3 and L4.

2. If the drill is employed with hose reel equipment it is unnecessary for No. 1 to lay out the hose reel hose in a long bight at the foot of the ladder.

Hose reel hose may be carried up a ladder by placing the sling, which may be attached to the nozzle, over the shoulder. Alternatively, the arm may be placed through a large overhand knot, which may be formed by using the first metre (approximately) of hose.

Effecting a rescue by means of an escape   Drill E4
A short extension ladder and a lowering
line (Five men)

1. It is not permissible to use a live person when carrying out Drill E4, a dummy must be used to simulate the rescued person.

2. When a Neil Robertson or Paraguard stretcher is used the method of securing the lowering line to the short extension ladder detailed below will not apply, as provision for attaching the line to the ring of the stretcher will have been made locally. The method of securing the dummy to the short extension ladder will also not apply.

Preliminary detail. As given in PD3.

'Get to work'. The escape is slipped and pitched to the appropriate floor as in Drills E1 and E2 with the ladders slightly lowered out in the carriage. Meanwhile No. 5 provides a short extension ladder, lowering line, guy line and short line. Nos. 1 and 2 man the levers while No. 3, with the main section of a short extension ladder and a short line, ascends the escape and enters the building. No. 4 mounts the escape and No. 1 passes to him the guyline and the running end of the lowering line over the levers.

No. 4 then ascends the escape, passes the end of the lowering line between the fifth and sixth rounds from the head of the escape. He then enters the building and takes the line with him. No. 3 assisted by No. 4 secures the dummy to the short extension ladder as detailed in Drill M4.

No. 4 makes a chair knot and assisted by No. 3 attaches the line to the lowering ladder as follows:

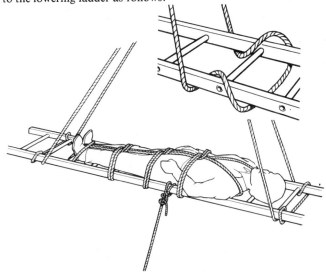

The two bights of the knot should be of equal length and when spread out should be about one and a half times the length of the ladder. The head of the ladder is then raised slightly and one bight passed over the end of the ladder, the centre of the bight being brought up from below between the two rounds immediately above the dummy's head. This portion of the bight is then passed over the upper round and outside the ends of the strings. The line is then adjusted so that the bight pulls above the dummy's head.

The other bight is passed over the foot of the ladder in the same manner with the centre of the bight being brought up between the two rounds immediately below the dummy's feet and similarly secured.

If necessary the relative lengths of the two bights are adjusted so that when the ladder is lowered, the dummy's head is kept slightly higher than its feet. No. 3 then bends the guy-line on to the centre of the outer string of the short extension ladder using a round turn and two half hitches and, with the arm fully extended, drops the line from the window. (This method of attaching the guy-line ensures that when it is pulled from below, the ladder cannot rotate and the heel is kept away from the building.)

Meanwhile as soon as No.4 has left the head of the escape, with No.5 manning the levers, Nos.1 and 2 heave up fully in the carriage and extend the escape into the window immediately above that from which the rescue is to be made; the chocks are, if necessary, to be adjusted during this manoeuvre. No.1 takes a full turn of the lowering line around the lever rail with the line leading over the top, whilst No.5 mans the guy line. No.2 mans the levers.

When the lines are correctly applied and all members of the crew are ready, Nos.3 and 4 lift the short extension ladder over the sill and guide it clear of the escape, while No.1 takes the strain on the lowering line. (The heel of the ladder, i.e. the feet of the dummy, is to be passed through the window first). When ready, No.1 gives the order 'Start to lower'.

No.1 lowers, controlling the line by paying it out in a hand over hand movement, each hand gripping the line alternately (the line must not be allowed to run through both hands at once), while No.5 maintains a steady, but not excessive, strain on the guy line, to keep the lowering ladder clear of the building. When the ladder reaches the ground, No.2 goes forward to assist No. 5 to steady it and to remove the dummy.

'Make up'. Nos.1 and 2 clear the line from the escape. Nos.2 and 5 man the levers whilst No.1 houses the escape until it can be repitched to the window from which the rescue has been effected. No.1 assists No.5 on the levers whilst No.2 lowers out in the carriage until the head is resting in the window. The chocks must be adjusted as necessary. No.3 descends followed by No.4.
The escape is then made up as in Drills E1 and E2

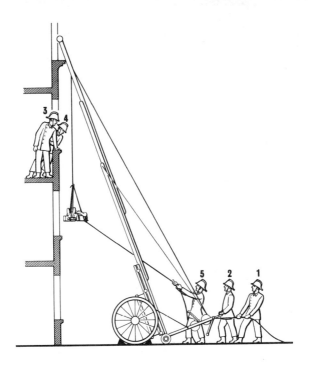

Notes:

1. If a rescue has to be made from the top floor it will be necessary to repitch the escape so that the head rests against the face of the building. Under these circumstances No.5 must ensure that whilst the ladder is being lowered, he does not pull excessively on the guy line which could cause the escape to slide across the face of the building.

2. Whilst Nos.1, 2 and 5 are repitching the escape a very firm grip must be kept on the lever rail while the head of the escape is not resting.

3. Where special slings are available for lowering, they may be used with, or without, a short extension ladder instead of the chair knot provided the loops are of suficient length.

4. This drill may also be carried out using an extension ladder instead of an escape, in which case the lowering line should be led over an appropriate round, down the front of the ladder, and a turn should be taken round the jack beam or the bottom round as appropriate. No.2 should remain at the heel of the ladder until lowering is complete.

5. Because abrasion may occur between the lowering line and the round it is advisable to use a line/round protector. This is not essential in operational use.

Bridging the escape (Four men)   Drill E5

Preliminary detail. As given in PD3.

'Get to work'. The escape is slipped as detailed in Drill E1. With No.1 on the nearside carriage wheel, No.2 on the offside carriage wheel and Nos.3 and 4 on the levers, the escape is manhandled into the required position for bridging. No.1 and 2 put down all wheel chocks and No.1 adjusts the heel chain and/or carriage stops to permit the ladder to be lowered out in the carriage to its fullest extent. Nos.1 and 2 man the carriage gear and lower the ladder fully out in the carriage.

Nos.1 and 2 extend the ladders to the required length (see safety Notes below), No.4 giving the order 'Well'.
The head of the escape is then lowered gently into position, utilising additional men. Nos.1 and 2 man the levers, their weight being maintained throughout the period during which the escape is bridged.

'Make up'. The head of the escape is raised by bearing down on the levers and lowering the lever wheels to the ground, utilising additional men if available. Nos. 1 and 2 man the carriage gear and heave the escape up in the carriage until sufficient elevation is reached for the ladders to be housed. Nos.1 and 2 man the extending gear and house the ladders, any additional men then being released. Nos.1 and 2 heave the escape up fully in the carriage, if necessary, and No.1 re-adjusts the heel chain. Nos.1 and 2 remove the wheel chocks and all four members of the crew manoeuvre the escape into position for mounting on the appliance. The escape is then mounted on the appliance as in Drill E1.

Notes:

Safety

1. Where there is a likelihood of the escape running back, the heel must be supported to take the backward thrust. A short extension ladder if available could be used for this purpose: if one is not available, the weight of the men manning the levers

should be maintained throughout the period the escape is bridged.

2. If the head of the escape cannot be raised to allow the ladders to lower under their own weight, a line should be secured to the bottom round of the top extension, which should be pulled back until sufficient length of ladder has been taken off to allow the head of the escape to be raised.

3. Except in emergency there should not be more than two men on the escape at any one time (one man per extension other than on a rescue drill).
See also the note 39 (a), (b), (c), (d), (e) and (g) on page 68.

Extension Ladder Drills

Slipping and pitching a 9m or 10.5m Ladder (Three men)   Drill L1

Preliminary detail. As given in PD2.

'Get to work'. No.1 gives the order *'Stand by to Slip'*. The crew dismount and No.1 and/or No.3 release the fastenings. When ready No.1 gives the order *'Slip'*, No.3 grips the heel of the ladder and, assisted by Nos.1 and 2 at the rear of the appliance, eases it backwards until the head of the ladder is within a distance of about two rounds from the gantry. Nos.1 and 2 lift the ladder clear of the appliance.

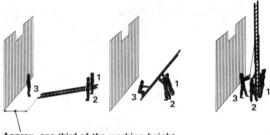

Approx. one third of the working height

Nos.1 and 2 at the head and No.3 at the heel carry the ladder to the required position at right angles to the face of the building with the heel approximately one third of the working height from the base of the building. Making certain that the correct side of the ladder is uppermost the heel of the ladder is placed on the ground. No.3 places both feet on the bottom round and pulls with his hands on a higher round.

No.1 gives the order *'under run'* and Nos.1 and 2 raise the ladder to the vertical position by underrunning with both arms fully extended and working closely together.

No.1 gives the order to *'Extend'*. No.3, by means of the line, estends the ladder to the required height, No.1 giving the order *'Well'* followed by *'Lower'*, and engages the pawls by placing his arm round the outside of a string and pulling on the line. Nos.1 and 2 steady the ladder while it is being extended. The ladder is then carefully placed into the window or against the building and the heel adjusted to give a safe working angle.

'Make up'. Nos.1, 2 and 3 take up their previous positions at the heel and pull the ladder into a vertical position No.1 gives the order *'Extend to lower'* followed by *'Well'* when sufficiently extended and *'Lower'* to house the extension. No.3, by means of the line, raises the extension slightly to trip the pawls, and then houses the extension. No.1 ensures that the pawls engage on the bottom or the second round. No.3 then places both feet on the bottom round, throws his weight backward and pulls with his hands on a higher round. Nos.1 and 2 lower the head of the ladder by underrunning. The crew then carry the ladder on to the gantry and all three members push the ladder into the riding position. No.1 and/or No.3 secures the fastenings after which a check is made by attempting to slip the ladder.

The crew then mount, No.1 reporting to the officer in charge.

Slipping and Pitching a 9m or 10.5m   Drill L2
Ladder (Four men)

Preliminary detail. As given in PD3.

'Get to work'. No.1 gives the order *'Stand by to Slip'*. The crew dismount, No. 1 and/or No.3 release the fastenings and No.1 gives the order *'Slip'*. Nos.3 and 4 grip the heel of the ladder and, assisted by Nos.1 and 2 at the rear of the appliance, ease it backwards until the head is within a distance of about two rounds from the gantry. Nos.1 and 2 lift the ladder clear of the appliance grasping it firmly.

Nos.1 and 2 at the head, Nos.3 and 4 at the heel, carry the ladder to the required position at right angles to the face of the building with the heel approximately one-third of the working ehight from the base of the building. After making certain that the correct side of the ladder is uppermost the heel of the ladder is placed on the ground. Nos.3 and 4 place their inner feet on the bottom round, i.e. the right foot of No.3 and the left foot of No.4 and pull with their hands on a higher round, and Nos.1 and 2 raise the ladder to the vertical position by underrunning.

No.1 orders *'Extend'*, No.3 by means of the line, extends the ladder to the required height. No.1 gives the orders *'Well'* when sufficiently extended and *'Lower'* to house the extension onto the pawls and No.4 doubles to the front of the ladder and trips the pawls. Meanwhile Nos.1 and 2 steady the ladder while it is being extended. The ladder is then carefully placed into the window or against the building and the heel adjusted to give a safe working angle.

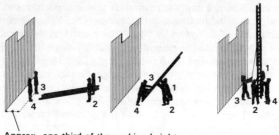

Approx. one third of the working height

'Make up'. Nos.1,2, 3 and 4 take up their previous positions at the heel and pull the ladder into a vertical position. No.1 gives the order *'Extend to lower'*. No.3, by means of the line, raises the extension slightly to trip the pawls. No.1 gives the order *'Well'* followed by *'Lower'* and No.3 then houses the extension. No.4 ensures that the pawls engage on the bottom or the second round. Nos.3 and 4 place their inner feet on the bottom round, throw their weight backwards and pull with their hands on a higher round. Nos.1 and 2 lower the head of the ladder by underrunning. The crew then carry the ladder to the rear of the appliance. Nos.1 and 2 lift the head of the ladder on to the gantry and all four members of the crew push the ladder into the riding position. Nos.1 and/or No.3 secures the fastenings after which a check is made by attempting to slip the ladder.
The crew then mount, No.1 reporting to the officer in charge.

> *Note:* To extend a ladder on which the extending line lies on the working face of the main section, No.3 doubles to the front of the ladder, extends to the required height and No.4 trips the pawls. To house the extension, No.3 operates the line and No.1 sees that the pawls engage on the bottom or the second round. After housing the extension, No.3 returns to the back of the ladder and resumes his position with No.4 at the heel.

Slipping and pitching a 13.5m Ladder (Four men)

Drill L3

Preliminary detail. As given in PD3.

'Get to work'. The ladder is slipped from the appliance and positioned to the building as detailed in drill L.2.
Nos.3 and 4 release the props from the clips, then support the heel with one foot each (their inside feet) on the jack beam outside the

strings and, with the props on the outer side of the body, pull on them by throwing their weight backwards as Nos.1 asnd 2 underrun and raise the ladder. Nos.3 and 4 continue to support the heel until the ladder has reached the vertical position at which time Nos.1 and 2 take over the footing with their outside feet. Nos.3 and 4 rest the props on the ground in line with each other and with the strings between the ladder and the building.

If it is necessary to plumb the ladder, No.1 gives the order to No.2 *'Plumb, left'*, *'Plumb, right'* and No.2 plumbs the ladder by adjusting the appropriate jack. No.1 gives the order *'Well'* when the ladder is vertical.

No.3 steadies the props and No.1 steadies the ladder from the front footing by straddling the base of the ladder, both feet on the jack beam one outside each of the 'strings' No.1 gives the order to extend, No.2 and 4 at the rear extend the ladder to the required height by hauling on the line. No.1 gives the order *'Well'* followed by *'lower'* and No.2 houses the extension slightly to engage the pawls. Nos.3 and 4 then lift on the props and, assisted by Nos.1 and 2 at the heel of the ladder, lower the head of the ladder carefully into the window or against the building. Nos.3 and 4 place the props on the ground in the best position to support the ladder, about 2/3 of the distance from the base of the ladder to the wall. No.2 checks the plumbing and readjusts if necessary.

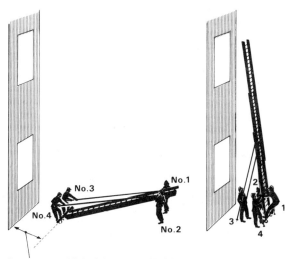

Approx. one third of the working height

'Make up'. No.1 supports the heel of the ladder and Nos.3 and 4 lift upwards with the props to clear the head of the ladder from the building. Nos.3 and 4 then rest the props while No.2 at the rear of the ladder, on the orders of No.1, hauls on the line to clear the pawls, houses the extensions and ensures that the pawls engage on the bottom round.

No.2 centralises the plumbing, if necessary, Nos.3 and 4 push the props until the ladder is in a vertical position and take over the footing from Nos.1 and 2.

Nos.1 and 2 then underrun the ladder assisted by Nos.3 and 4 throwing their weight backwards on the props. When the ladder is on the ground, Nos.3 and 4 replace the props in the clips.

The ladder is then returned to the appliance as detailed in L.2. The crew then mount, No.1 reporting to the officer in charge.

Notes:

1. Where the ladder is carried on the appliance with the main section down, it should be turned over after removal from the appliance so that the extensions are underneath when it is placed on the ground.

2. When the ladder is used on soft or sloping ground, particular care should be taken in placing and supervising the props.

Pitching a 13.5m Ladder in a Confined space   Drill L4 (Four men)

Preliminary detail. As given in PD 3

'Get to work'. The ladder slipped from the appliance as in Drill L2. Nos. 1 and 2 at the head and Nos. 3 and 4 at the heel carry the ladder to the required position and place it on the ground parallel to the face of the building. With the furthest jack pad approximately one third of the working height from the building. After making sure that the correct side of the ladder is uppermost, the heel of the ladder is placed on the ground. The crew then underrun the ladder as in drill L.3.(Fig.1)

When the ladder is in the vertical position with Nos.1 and 2 grasping the strings and Nos. 3 and 4 grasping the props (Fig.2) No. 1 gives the order *'Tilt' No.3* or *'Tilt' No.4* as appropriate (the man nearest to the building). The named man moves to a position slightly out of line with the strings with his back to the face of the building (Fig. 3) and gently pushes upwards on his pole so that the ladder pivots on the spur or jack at the base of the far away string, with No. 1 or 2 as appropriate (the man furthest from the building) standing on the jack beam and grasping the strings (Fig.4).

The ladder is turned by No. 1 or 2 as appropriate (the man nearest the building) to face the building (Fig. 5). As the ladder is being turned the *'tilt'* is maintained by both men on the props, initially by the man at the face of the building and secondly by the man on the other prop. Nos.3 or 4, as appropriate, changing his position as required to join the man already at the face of the building (Fig. 6), the ladder is then plumbed if necessary and extended as in Drill L3.

'Make up'. The ladder is housed as detailed in drill L3. but, before it is under-run to the ground it should be turned parallel with the building as detailed above but in the reverse direction. The ladder is then returned to the appliance and checked secure by attempting to *'slip'*, the crew then mount, No.1 reporting to the officer-in-charge.

Fig. 1

Fig. 2

Fig. 3

Fig. 4
88

Fig. 5

Fig. 6

89

Effecting a Rescue by Carrying Down (Three or Four men)
Drill L5

Preliminary detail. As given in PD 2 for a 3-man crew or PD3 for a 4-man crew.

'Get to work'. The ladder is removed from the appliance and pitched as detailed in Drills L1, L2, L3 or L4.
For a three-man crew. No.3 mounts the ladder followed by No.1. No.3 then effects the rescue by carrying down. No.2 must not leave the heel of the ladder.

For a four-man crew. No.3 mounts the ladder followed by No.4. No.3 then effects the rescue by carrying down. No.2 must not leave the heel of the ladder.

'Make up'. The ladder is made up as detailed in Drills L1, L2, L3 or L4. The crew then mount, No.1 reporting to the officer in charge.

Bridging A 10.5 m Ladder (Four men)
Drill L6

Preliminary detail. As given in PD 3

'Get to work'. The ladder is slipped from the appliance as in L2. The crew carry the ladder to the required position placing it on the ground with the working face uppermost and the head of the ladder nearest to the gap to be bridged, 1m from the edge.
Nos.1 and 2 provide a short extension ladder, or two sections of a triple extension ladder, and a long hydrant key. They then construct a short step ladder using a pocket line to secure the head. The step ladder is then positioned adjacent to the head of the 10.5m ladder and the hydrant key is placed horizontally across convenient rounds of the step ladder, adjacent to the strings nearest the gap to be bridged.

Nos. 3 and 4 lift the head of the 10.5m ladder on to the hydrant key whilst Nos. 1 and 2 support the step ladder footing each section in the approved manner. Nos. 3 and 4 then double to the heel of the 10.5m ladder and No. 3 assisted, if necessary, by No. 4 extends the ladder to the required length. No. 4 then lashes the two sections of the 10.5m ladder together with a pocket line around two convenient rounds adjacent to the pawls. Nos. 3 and 4 lift the heel of the ladder and push the head smartly over the hydrant key and across the gap to be bridged, with a continuous movement until the head is beyond the contact point, the head of the ladder is then lowered gently into position on the far side.

Nos. 3 and 4 take the weight of the 10.5m ladder, whilst Nos. 1 and 2 remove the hydrant key and the step ladder, and then place the heel on the ground. The heel of the 105 ladder must be attended at all times when personnel are crossing the gap.

'Make up'. Nos. 3 and 4 lift the heel of the 10.5m ladder whilst Nos. 1 and 2 replace the step ladder and reposition the hydrant key adjacent to the strings furthest from the gap.

With Nos. 1 and 2 supporting the step ladder Nos. 3 and 4 take a firm hold of the heel of the 10.5m ladder and, applying a downward pressure, pull away from the gap in a continuous movement until No. 1 gives the order *'Well'* when the head of ladder is within 1m of the hydrant key. Nos. 1 and 2 then transfer their hold to to 10.5m ladder lifting the head clear of the step ladder. No. 1 gives the order *'lower'* and all members of the crew place the ladder on the ground. No. 4 removes the lashing from the 10.5m ladder and, assisted by No. 3 makes up the ladder and replaces it on the appliance. Nos. 1

and 2 dismantle the step ladder and return all equipment to the appliance.

Notes: (see also Note 39 (a),(f) and (g) on page 68)

1. This method is not suitable for bridging gaps in excess of 6m or to heights above 3m.

2. When footing the short extension sections Nos.1 and 2 should apply weight and force against the movement of the 10.5m ladder whichever direction it is travelling.

3. Additional men should be used at the heel of the 10.5m ladder when passing it over the gap and when retrieving it.

4. Men crossing a bridged ladder should move carefully to avoid undue oscillation of the ladder.

Removing and splitting a 10.5m ladder (Four men)　　　　　　　Drill L7

Preliminary details. As given in PD 3

'**Get to work**'. The ladder is slipped from the appliance as in Drill L2 and placed on the ground about 2m to the rear of the appliance. No.3 disconnects both snap hooks and places them between the rounds clear of the extending section.

No.1 at the head and No.3 at the heel move the extending section towards the head of the main ladder, No.3 holding the pawls to clear them, and then draw the extending section towards the heel of the main ladder and clear of it.

Nos.1 and 3 carry the section to the required position when the heel is placed on the ground. No.3 places both feet on the bottom round and pulls with his hands on a higher round while No.1 raises the ladder by underrruning.

The section is then gently lowered into the window or against the building and the heel adjusted to give a safe working angle approximately one third of the working height from the base of the building.

Meanwhile No.4 passes one line under the bottom round of the main ladder and secures both snap hooks together. Nos.2 and 4 carry the main ladder to the required position and pitch it in a similar manner as performed by Nos.1 and 3 with their section. No.4 ensures that the line does not drag.

'**Make up**'. Nos.1 and 3 and Nos.2 and 4 lower their respective sections by reversing the above procedure, carry the sections to their original position at the rear of the appliance and place them on the ground. Nos.1 and 2 at the head and Nos.3 and 4 at the heel place the head of the extending section under the running guides of the main ladder and push the section into position. No.3 connects both snap hooks and ensure that the pawls are engaged on the main ladder.

After the ladder is made up, No.1 checks that the snap hooks are correctly secured and the ladder is then pitched and extended to its full working height to ensure that the extension is correctly fitted to the main ladder and the pawls operate correctly.

The ladder is then made up and replaced on the appliance as in Drill L2, the crew mount, No.1 reporting to the officer in charge.

Note: The drill may be performed by two men; is so No.1 takes on the duties of Nos.1 and 2, and No.2 takes on the duties of Nos.3 and 4. After re-assembly, additional men will be required to check the correct operation of the ladder.

Turntable Ladder Drills

Notes on turntable ladder drills

1. Safety

(a) In gusty or strong wind conditions, turntable ladders (TLs) should only be used for operational purposes. Guy lines should be used where provided. When it is necessary to operate a TL in a strong wind for operational purposes, at least two men should be detailed to hold each line which should never be made fast at its running end. Vertical pull on the head of the ladder should be kept to a minumum by giving as wide an angle as possible to the lines. The strain on a guy line should be no more than is necessary to counter the effect of the wind. If a ladder is to be used as a water tower in a strong wind nobody should be allowed on the ladder and the monitor should be controlled by lines. Officers-in-charge should remember, if drilling in a sheltered area, that wind conditions above roof level may be gusty or stronger than on the ground.

(b) Manual axle locks, where fitted, should always be engaged before the jacks are lowered to the ground.

(c) Before positioning a TL and lowering jacks a check should be made of any possible ground hazards, not only under the vehicle, but also in the adjacent areas where out-span jacks are liable to come to rest.

(d) Although as many members of the crew as possible should be TL operators it is inevitable that men who are not qualified will form part of a crew. The fact that a ''change-round'' (see Page 9) is included in the drill should not be taken to mean that unqualified men should operate a ladder.

(e) To relieve the jet-reacton of the monitor in an emergency the hose-line should incorporate a special control valve at the coupling nearest to the ladder.

The pressure should not be released too suddenly as the severe reduction in jet-reaction could cause the ladder to sway considerably.

(f) Communication between the ground operator and the head of the ladder shall be maintained at all times.

(g) Every opportunity should be taken to carry out TL drills at other premises in addition to drill yards and to give TL operators maximum experience under all conditions, especially the need to practice safety procedures.

(h) Whenever a TL is to be extended with a man aloft No. 3 secures himself to the safety ring at the head of the ladder by the safety belt. He makes certain that his toes do not protrude between the rounds of the section to which the platform is attached. After satisfying himself that the communications equipment is operative, he should then extend his left arm sideways and horizontally to its fullest extent (to show that he is secure, correctly positioned and ready for the ladder to be extended). No. 2 must not extend the ladder until this signal has been received and No. 3 has both hands back on the handrail. Ladders must only be operated when the man is standing on the platform, and showing a clean pair of heels. TL operators should never *'shoot-up'* a man directly into the chosen area but should extend parallel to the building and train in slowly. Similarly when housing with a man aloft operators should train away before doing so. This should ensure that the man at the head of the ladder does not, at any time, pass into, or through, dangerous conditions.

It is not suggested that the practice of *'shooting-up'* should be mandatory for all occasions and circumstances, but rather it should be used at the discretion of the ladder operator.

NB

(i) Turntable ladder operators are fully responsible for the safe operation of their appliance and for the safekeeping of any personnel who may be working on the ladder.

(j) Personnel should not mount the ladder section of the appliance without the permission of the operator.

(k) On each occasion, prior to commencing any sequence of operations, the operator should visually check all sections of the ladder to ensure that nobody is standing on the ladder other than on the platform, showing a clean pair of heels, or in the cage.

2. General

Turntable ladder cages

Some ladders are supplied with rescue cages which are, or can be, fitted to the head of the ladders. Drill should be carried out with these cages by adapting the existing drills in this section, always following the manufacturers instructions.

Turntable Ladder Drills

As a water-tower   Drill T1
(Three men plus pump's crew)

Notes:

(a) A pump which is supplying a TL monitor should not be used to supply any other appliances or equipment. For the purposes of these drills, an *'independent'* pump is taken to be a pump which is on the TL body but driven by an engine which is not the road engine, a light portable pump, or on a completely separate fire fighting appliance.

(b) No. 3 must always wear a TL safety belt and conspicuity armband.

Preliminary drill. As given in PD2

'Get to work' The crew dismounts, No. 2 first engaging the ladder power take off.

Where hydraulically operated jacks and axle locks are fitted, No. 2 operates all jacks and axle locks. Nos. 1 and 3 check the jacks are resting correctly whilst No. 2 remains at the console.

If manual axle locks and jacks are fitted No. 2 doubles to the rear of the appliance and engages the axle locks.

No. 1 lowers the ground jacks on the nearside and places a chock at the rear of the nearside rear wheel. No. 3 lowers the ground jacks on the offside and places a chock at the front of the offside rear wheel. No. 2 making the final adjustments.

> *Note.* Where jacking lifts the rear wheels completely off the ground these chocks should be placed, as detailed, on the front wheels. When working on a hill both chocks should be placed on the downhill side of the wheels).

If the hose cannot be paid out of the locker, Nos. 1 and 3 remove the hose and carry it to the rear of the ladders. No. 2 elevates the ladders as required, No. 3 releases the fly ladder (if fitted) and climbs to the head of the ladder, releases the platform and hooks himself onto the ring provided. No. 1 provides himself with a hose becket, connects the hose to the coupling of the fixed pipe on the upper extension and secures the hose to the pipe with the hose becket.

He then replaces the fly ladder, No. 2 extends the ladder as required, No. 1 clears the hose from the ground and ensures it does not foul the ladder, and fixes the pressure relief valve to the coupling lying at the heel of the ladder.

The independent pump is got to work by a pump's crew as detailed in P2.

When ready No. 3 gives the order *'water on'* to No. 2 who passes it on to the No. 1 of the pump's crew.

'Knock off' or **'Knock off'** and **'make up'** No. 3 gives the order *'Knock off'* or *'Knock off'* and *'make up'* to No. 2 who passes the order to No. 1 of the pump's crew. No. 2 of the pump's crew will shut down the delivery

'Make up' The pump's crew will make up a detailed in P2.

When the flow has stopped No. 1 opens the pressure relief valve, breaks the coupling nearest the heel of the ladder.

No. 2 houses the ladder, No. 1 clearing the hose. When the ladder is housed No. 1 releases the fly ladder takes off the hose becket and disconnects the hose from the fixed pipe.

No. 3 unhooks himself, houses the platform, descends to the ground and replaces the fly ladder.

No. 2 depresses the ladders on to the headrest, hydraulically houses the jacks disengages the axle locks and the power take-off.

Nos. 1 and 3 underrun and make up the hose, replace the hose, becket and chocks (and take up the jacks where they are manually retracted). The crew then mount, No. 1 reporting to the officer in charge.

Replacing a burst length of hose   Drill T2
(Three men plus pump's crew)

The ladder will be at work as in Drill T1

'Get to work' No. 3 of the TL crew gives the order *'Knock off'* to his No. 2 who passes the order to the No. 1 of the pump's crew. No. 2 trains the ladder away from the building and houses it, No. 1 opening the pressure relief valve and clearing the hose. The pump's crew provide and lay out a replacement length of hose.

When the ladder is housed No. 1 releases the fly ladder and the hose straps, leaving the becket in position, disconnects the burst length from the fixed length and connects the replacement length securing it to the becket then replaces the fly ladder. The pump's crew clear away the burst length, connect the replacement length to the pressure relief valve and close the valve. An overhand knot is tied in each end of the burst length.

On receiving the signal from No. 3, No. 2 extends the ladder to the required height, pawls and trains in, No. 1 clearing the hose. No. 3 gives the order *'Water on'* to his No. 2 who passes the order to No. 1 of the pump's crew.

Effecting a rescue   Drill T3
(Three men)

Notes:

1. All TLs should be issued with a special rescue line 70m long. This line must always be used when a TL is used to carry out a rescue by lowering by line. The line should be carried on the appliance made up on a cradle or reel with the sling and tail-line attached. Normally the line is permanently rove through a pulley block having a specially shaped hook and this is kept with the line in the cradle. However, some appliances have a fixed snatch block fitted permanently to the under-side of the head of the top extension into which the line is placed before elevating. (The guy line may also be attached with the sling and tail line).

97

2.   Sufficient quantity of line to reach from the heel of the ladder to the front of the appliance should be pulled clear and placed in the centre of the cradle with the sling and tail line. the hook must be attached to the eye-ring, the large end uppermost. The pulley-block must be suspended from the small end at the lower part of the hook and the hook-jaw must face outward from the ladder. If the hook is placed in any other position it is possible for it to foul the ladder when it is being extended and for it to be wrenched open.

3.   When the line, sling and tail line have been attached to the head of the ladder the cradle is then placed in line with and behind the bollard (brake cleat) and, as the ladder is trained, this position is maintained by moving the cradle. The line is passed through the fairlead and allowed to pay out under the control of No. 1, but should not be passed round the bollard until No. 3 gives the order *'take up the slack'*.

4.   TLs must not be extended or housed whilst a dummy is being rescued by this method. The correct method is to swing the dummy clear of the building by training the ladder away.

5.   When a guy line is used to steady the sling lowering, a 4th man must be available to man the guy line, to receive the dummy and to release the rescue sling.

Preliminary detail as in PD2

'Get to Work' The ladder is prepared for operation as in Drill T1

No. 3 provides the rescue line and cradle and places them at the rear of the appliance (see Note 3). No. 1 provides, attaches and steadies the stirrup, No. 3 takes the pulley-block to the front of the appliance, steps on the stirrup and hooks it onto the eye-ring at the head of the top extension (see Note 2). No. 3 steps down and No. 1 disengages the stirrup.

No. 2 elevates the ladder, No. 3 releases the fly-ladder (if fitted) climbs the ladder, releases the platform and hooks himself on to the ring provided. No. 1 replaces the fly ladder. On receiving the signal from No. 3, No. 2 extends the ladder to the required height, No. 1 maintaining control of the line.

No. 3 enters the building, places the dummy in the sling, gives the order *'take up the slack'* and manoeuvres the dummy onto the sill. No. 1 passes the line through the fairlead, takes up the slack, and then takes one or two turns round the bollard. No. 2 trains the ladder away from the building, No. 3 controlling the swing of the dummy with the tail line. No. 1 controls the rescue line, hand over hand, lowering the dummy until it is received at ground level (see Note No. 5).

Plates

Plate 1. The position of 'Attention' from the front.

Plate 2. The position of 'Attention' from the side.

Plate 3. The position of 'Stand at Ease' from the rear.

Plate 4. Saluting to the front.

Plate 5. The correct method of running out rolled hose (left),
and (right) preparing to run out a length of Dutch-rolled hose.

Plate 6. The correct method of holding a branch (two men).

Plate 7. The correct method of tightening a suction coupling.

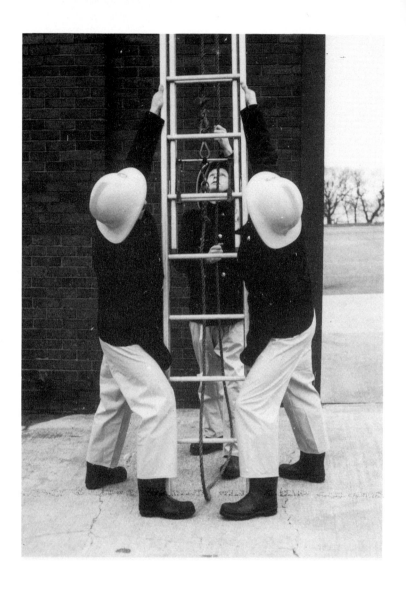

Plate 8. The correct method of holding the heel of a 10.5m ladder while it is being extended.

Plate 9. The correct method of footing a ladder (one man).

Plate 10. The correct method of footing a ladder (two men).

Plate 11. The correct method of carrying down. The head is well forward, allowing the dummy to rest squarely on the shoulders and the rescuer's arms and legs are moving in unison.

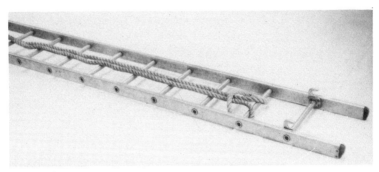

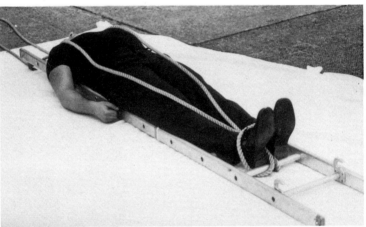

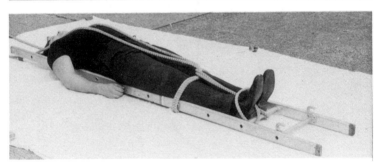

Plate 12. The initial stages of the correct method of applying the lashing to secure a patient to the main ladder of a short extension or triple extension ladder.

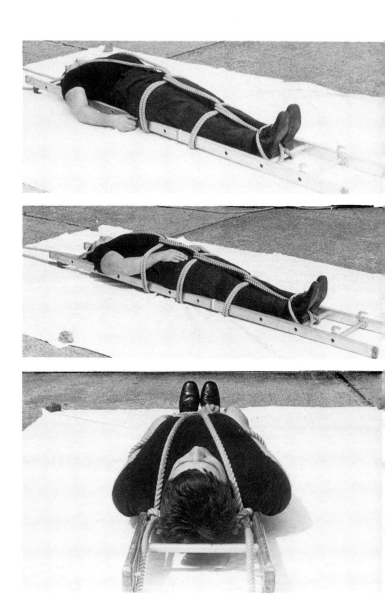

Plate 13. The correct method of applying the lashing to secure a patient to the main ladder of a short extension of triple extension ladder in the final stages.

Plate 14. The correct method of attaching a lowering line and a guy line when either lowering or hauling up vertically.

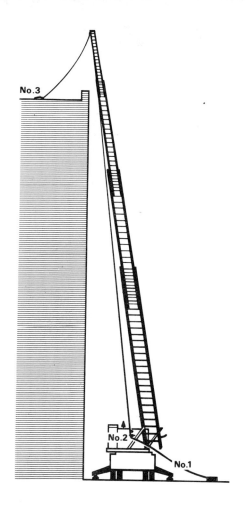

'Make up'

On the order *'make up'*, No. 2 retrains the head of the ladder to the building and No. 3 remounts the ladder, hooks himself onto the ring provided and gives the signal to No. 2. No. 2 houses the ladder. No. 1 releases the fly ladder, No. 3 unhooks and descends to the ground, replacing the fly ladder. No. 2 depresses the ladder onto the headrest, hydraulically takes up the jacks and axle locks and disengages the power take-off. Nos. 1 and 3 make up the line and chocks and, where fitted, house the manual jacks.

The crew then mount, No. 1 reporting to the officer in charge.

Hydraulic platform drills

Notes on hydraulic platform drills

1. Safety

(a) Every opportunity should be taken to carry out hydraulic platform (HP) drills at other premises in addition to drill yards, and to give HP operators maximum experience under all conditions, especially the need to practice safety procedures.

(b) HP operators are fully responsible for the safe operation of their appliance and for the safekeeping of any personnel who may be working on the appliance.

(c) When an HP is working on level ground the front wheels should be chocked as detailed in Drill HP1. When an HP is working on a hill both chocks should be placed on the downhill side of the front wheels.

(d) The appliance should be levelled from side to side by means of the jacks to compensate for any camber. When the appliance is sited on a hill, by positioning it to face uphill, the jacks can also be used to level the appliance front to rear as far as practicable. See also TL Note (c).

(e) In siting the appliance facing uphill the operator must take into account the fact that if, after the deployment of the jacks the slope of the chassis exceeds the limit of the level indicator (normally five degrees), the booms may not be able to train at maximum projection over the rear of the appliance with the cage fully loaded.

(f) Chocks should never be adjusted once operation of the booms has begun.

(g) A long line should always be taken aloft in the cage so that any additional gear may be hauled up as necessary.

(h) When in operation an HP should have two operators with the appliance. One operator in the platform cage and one operator (driver) at the ground controls to take over in an emergency.

(i) When manoeuvres are being carried out the ground operator must keep constant watch. He must be prepared to over-ride the cage control in an emergency.

(j) Communication between the ground operator and the platform cage shall be maintained at all times.

(k) The weight of personnel and equipment should be taken into account when determining the load. The maximum limits must never be exceeded.

2. General

(a) The water pipes should be drained as appropriate by means of the facilities provided.

(b) Siting the appliance, plumbing and appliance operations in general are the responsibility of the ground operator (No.2). Lowering of the jacks and their correct alignment are the responsibility of Nos. 1 and 3 (see TL Note 1 (b)).

As a water tower   Drill HP 1
(Three men plus pump's crew)

Preliminary details as given in PD2.

'Get to work' The crew dismount, No. 2 first engaging the power take off and setting the hand-throttle. No. 1 places a chock in front of the nearside front wheel, No. 3 places a chock behind the off-side front wheel (except when appliance is working on a hill, see Note 1c). Nos. 1 and 3 lower the jacks in unison ensuring they come to rest on solid ground and are extended correctly. Nos. 1 and 3 enter the cage, No. 3 carrying a long line. No. 1 operates the cage to the required position whilst No. 2 remains by the ground controls carrying out instructions from No. 1. The water is provided as in Drill T1.

'Knock off and 'make up' No. 1 gives the order, *'Knock off' and 'make up'* to No. 2 who passes it to No. 1 of the pump's crew, No. 1 lowers the cage to the ground and drains the upper section water-pipe. No. 3 dismounts and drains the lower section. When this is completed No. 1 lowers the booms onto the headrest. Nos. 1 and 3 raise the jacks and see they are housed correctly. No. 2 replaces chocks and disengages the power take-off. After making up lines and other equipment used the crew mount, No. 1 reports to the officer in charge.

Effecting a rescue   Drill HP2
(Three men)

Preliminary detail as given in PD2

'Get to Work' The hydraulic platform is got to work as described in Drill HP. 1 No. 1 raises the cage to the required position.

No. 3 enters the building to assist persons into the cage. No. 1 brings the cage to ground level, Nos. 1 and 3 assist persons to dismount.

'Make up' As detailed in Drill HP. 1 except water pipes will not require draining.

Miscellaneous Drills

Picking up drills

Note: Initial training in picking up should be commenced without overtrousers but, once personnel become proficient, overtrousers should be worn.

To pick up an insensible person (Two rescuers)

Drill M1

Formation of sections.

Personnel fall in single rank and number from the right in threes, each three forming a section.

'Fall in'	No. 2 stands fast. Nos. 1 and 3 fall in facing No. 2 three paces apart.
'Remove headgear'	The person (no. 3) who is to be picked up, removes his headgear and places it clear of operations.
'One'	No. 3 (who acts as the body) lies down on his back with his head pointing towards No. 2
'Two'	No. 2 steps forward and adjusts the *'body's'* arms and legs so that they point slightly outwards
'Three'	No. 1 standing at the feet of and facing No. 3 places his right foot between No. 3's thighs close to the crotch and kneels down with his left knee outside the right thigh.
'Four'	No. 2 kneels down with his left knee on the left of No. 3's head facing the direction of No. 3's feet.
'Five'	No. 2 supporting No. 3's head, assists No. 1 who will pull on No. 3's arms to raise the body to a sitting position.

On the orders 'Three' and 'Four'

On the order 'Five'

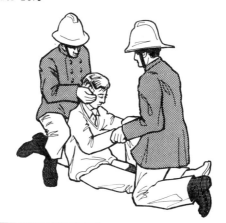

'Six'	Nos. 1 and 2 grip No. 3 under the armpits and around the chest respectively then, simultaneously, adopt a standing position keeping their backs straight and lifting No. 3 between them to vertical position.
'Seven'	Nos. 1 and 2 position their right knees together, side by side between No. 3's thighs.
'Eight'	No. 2 assisted by No. 1 holds No. 3 in the upright position taking the bulk of No. 3's weight on his right thigh.

'Nine'

No. 1 grips No. 3's right wrist with his left hand, bends slightly at the knees, places his right arm under the crotch and round the back of No. 3's right thigh and, assisted by No. 2, using No. 3's arm as a lever, pulls No. 3 across his shoulder. No. 2 supporting the hips of No. 3.

No. 1 then resumes an upright position, gets the body evenly balanced on his shoulders and transfers No. 3's right wrist to his right hand. Nos. 1 and 2 then pick up their dressing on the other sections doing the drill.

On the order 'Nine'

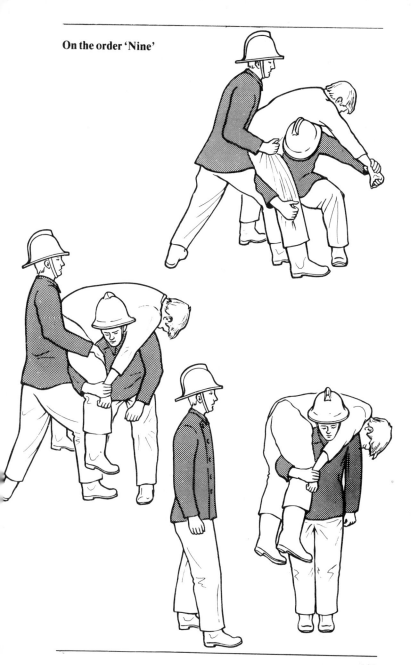

To lower an insensible person to the ground (two rescuers)

The body (No. 3) is being carried as above.
Nos. 1 and 2 stand facing each other at two paces distance (No. 1 carrying the body (No. 3)).

'One'	No. 1 takes one step with the right foot towards No. 2.
'Two'	No. 2 takes one step with his right foot towards No. 1 and braces his right knee and leg alongside No. 1's, placing his hands around No. 3's hips.
'Three'	No. 1 slightly bending his knees and keeping his back straight lowers No. 3 into a vertical position with No. 3's back facing No. 2, and with No. 3's legs straddling Nos. 1 and 2's knees.
'Four'	Nos. 1 and 2 grip No. 3 under the armpits and around the chest, respectively.
'Five'	Nos. 1 and 2 adopt a kneeling position simultaneously on left knees, keeping their backs straight and slowly lowering No. 3 through the sitting position, to a horizontal position on his back, No. 1 holding No. 3's arms and No. 2 supporting No. 3's shoulders and head.
'Six'	No. 2 straightens the body's arms and legs and resumes his position at the head of No. 3 (the body). No. 1 takes up a position at the feet of No. 3.
'Fall out'	No. 3 replaces headgear and the sections form up in single rank.

To pick up an insensible person (One rescuer)

Drill M2

Formation of sections.

Personnel fall in single rank and number from the right in twos, each two forming a section.

'Fall in'	Nos. 1 and 2 fall in facing each other three paces apart, No. 2 with his back to a convenient wall.
'Remove caps'	The person (No. 2) who is to be picked up removes his headgear and places it clear of operations.
'One'	No. 2 (who acts as the body) lies down in the prone position with his head towards No. 1 and feet touching the wall.

'Two'	No. 1 moves forward, places his hands under the armpits and lifts the body to a kneeling position (being careful not to drag the knees along the ground). At the same time he advances the right foot, bends the knee and allows the body to rest against it. He then stands with his hands under the body's armpits, with his left leg straight, a hollow back and head erect.
'Three'	No. 1 brings his left foot up to his right foot, bends down and interlaces his fingers low down behind the body's back

107

and lifts the body on to its feet, passing his right knee between the legs, supporting the weight of the body on his right thigh and using the weight of his own body to pin on the trunk against the wall.

TWO

THREE

No. 1 takes the body's right wrist in his left hand with the back of his right uppermost and with his arm extended in line with the shoulder, he then steps back with his left foot about 150mm, bends down, allowing the body's trunk to fall over his shoulders. He then places his right arm between the legs and, using the body's right arm as a lever pulls the body across his shoulders. He then resumes an upright position, balances the body evenly on his shoulders and transfers the body's right wrist to his right hand. He then picks up his dressing on the other sections doing the drill.

To lower an insensible person to the ground (one rescuer)

The body is being carried as above.

'One'   No. 1 withdraws his right arm from between the body's legs, passes it round the legs and at the same time grasps the body's right wrist with his left hand.

'Two'	No. 1 drops on to his left knee, swings the body's legs clear of his own across the front of his body, lowers it to a sitting position and allows his right hand to slide up the body to support the waist.
'Three'	After freeing the body's left arm, No. 1 places his right arm behind the body's shoulders, removes the body's right arm from behind his neck and lowers the body gently into a prone position, taking care that the head does not strike the ground. He straightens the body's arms and legs and then stands to attention at the body's head.

Notes on picking up drills.

1. Men should be proficient in picking up and lowering an insensible person before being allowed to carry down.

2. The unconscious person is usually carried on the right shoulder. The head of the ladder is usually pitched to the right hand side of the window opening, therefore carrying on the right shoulder ensures greater protection to the unconscious person's head. However, firemen should practice "left-handed" carries occasionally.

3. The weight of the person being carried should be distributed evenly on both shoulders, the head of the rescuer should be bent forward to allow this. Difficulty will be experienced in achieving this if the rescuer is wearing compressed air breathing apparatus.

Lowering by Line Drill

Notes on lowering by line drill

Safety

The following points must be adhered to when carrying out lowering by line drills.

1. The standard lowering drill sets outs the procedure at the floor from which the lowering is taking place, and in this case it is assumed that the men and equipment may have reached the floor to be used by means of the internal stairway in the tower.

2. The lowering drill may also be carried out in conjunction with escape or extension ladder drills, in which case the crew will slip and pitch in the usual way after which the ladder will be mounted by the crew and the line taken up with them or hauled aloft as appropriate.

Lowering by line under foot
(Three men)

A dummy is to be provided aloft to simulate the person to be rescued.

Preparation for lowering. When Nos. 1 and 3 are ready at the floor from which the lowering is to be carried out, No. 1 prepares the legs of the lowering line (or ties a chair knot), secures the line to the dummy and ensures that the guy line is properly secured to the lowering line with a clove hitch (one part above the splice and one below). No. 1 calls *'Stand from under'* and drops the guy line at arm's length from the window. Meanwhile No. 2 stands ready in the drill yard to take hold of the guy line when the running part is dropped. No. 3 clears the running part of the lowering line so that it will run free from kinks and entanglement.

Nos. 1 and 3 each grasp the dummy beneath the legs and armpits and raise it to the sill and allow it to rest across the sill with its trunk leaning back slightly inside the window, supported by No. 3.

When the dummy is in position on the sill, No. 1 leads the line from the dummy underneath the instep of his left foot and grips it firmly in his right hand, keeping his right arm straight and close to the body.

Position immediately before lowering. No. 1 now positions himself so that his body is at right angles to the window with his left foot

placed as close to the inner face of the structure as possible immediately beneath the window at floor level. The entire weight of No. 1's body should be over his left leg, which should be kept straight and braced against the sill and/or the wall below the sill. His feet are to be kept apart, his left hand gripping the outer edge and the underside of the sill.

Procedure for lowering. No. 3 then eases the dummy clear of the sill and No. 1 takes the weight. No. 1 holds the line, which passes underneath the instep of his left foot, in his right hand with the palm facing inwards towards his body, thumb in line with the lowering line. No. 3 positions himself so that he can look out of the window and give appropriate directions to No. 1 during the lowering. No. 3 rests the ball of his left foot lightly on, and at right angles to, the toe of No. 1's foot. This serves as an additional safety precaution, so that, if No. 1 should inadvertently relax the weight on his left foot, No. 3 will be able to apply pressure with the ball of his foot, checking the passage of the line.

No. 1 then, with caution, gradually releases sufficient weight from his left leg (by raising his heel slightly, not be bending his left knee, which must be kept stiff during the entire lowering operation) to allow the line to move. He lowers the dummy, controlling the rate of descent by means of the weight on his left leg and gripping the line with his right hand. Whilst lowering, No. 1 looks straight ahead and takes his directions from No. 3 until the dummy reaches the ground. No. 2 meanwhile controls the guy line to ensure that the dummy is kept clear of the structure. When the dummy reaches the ground, No. 2 clears the line from the dummy. No. 3 then calls out *'Stand from under'*, and drops the remainder of the line out of the window.

Notes:

1. The special sling used by some brigades in conjunction with lowering lines may be used as an alternative to the legs of the lowering line (or chair knot) referred to above.

2. When the line is carried aloft, if no line carrier is available the line must be made up in such a manner that the coils do not lie across the chest when slung over the shoulder.

Securing a Patient to a ladder

Lashing a patient (or dummy) to a short extension ladder (Two men) Drill M4

This lashing can be used whenever there is a need to rescue a patient from a height, a difficult location or to transport one over difficult terrain on a short extension ladder.

Prior to the drill the main ladder section of a short extension ladder or triple extension ladder and a short line is to be placed on the ground with a dummy (in the case of line lowering drills) or a live patient (in other circumstances) laid alongside, feet in line with the of the ladder.

'Formation of sections'. Men fall in in single rank and number from the right in twos, each two men forming a section.

'Fall in'	Two men of a section fall in facing one another, No. 1 at the feet and No. 2 at the head of the dummy or patient.
'One'	The dummy or patient is placed centrally on the ladder with the feet on a convenient round and the head towards the head of the ladder. (Where simulating the rescue of an injured person a third man should support the injured part).
'Two'	No. 1 takes the short line and assisted by No. 2 middles the line and bends the bight onto the round nearest the feet of the dummy or patient to secure them (Plate 12).
'Three'	Half hitches are taken around the ladder and the dummy or patient with both parts of the line three times—below the knees—at the hips—and slightly above the waist (Plate 13).
'Four'	The lines are then parted and taken one over each shoulder and secured to the round behind the shoulder or each with a clove hitch (Plate 13).
Make up 'One'	The line is removed by No. 1 assisted by No. 2 and the dummy or patient is raised from the ladder by No. 1 at the feet and No. 2 at the head and placed alongside the short extension ladder, or triple extension ladder, both men resuming the *'Fall in'* position.
'Two'	Both men return to the left of the single rank, take up their dressing and stand at ease.

1. If because of the position of the dummy or patient on the ladder, the securing round is too far down behind the shoulders to tie the clove hitches easily, a round turn may be taken at that round then tied off with clove hitches at the round above. Particular care should'be taken to ensure the safety and comfort when live patients are used.

2. Some form of protection, i.e. a fire tunic, should be placed on the ladder to support the head. In Drill E4 this in not practicable until the chair knot or lowering line is in position.

3. This method of lashing can be used in a vertical rescue situation, i.e. from shafts, sewers, cliffs, ships holds etc. when the Paraguard or Neil Robertson stretchers are not available. Negotiating narrow passageways, stairs, small openings, etc. should be encouraged. The means of lowering or hauling being provided by a separate line, the line to be secured to the head of the ladder by a bowline, the bight being passed beneath the top round and over and around the upper strings. A guy-line should be secured in a similar manner, above the bottom round to the heel of the ladder (Plate 14).

Breathing apparatus drill

The following drills are issued for guidance in the donning and starting-up of the apparatus. However, when manufacturers specify particular procedures (e.g. starting-up procedure), those instructions over-ride any guidance in this section. It is assumed that the general check has been carried out and, therefore, that the mask and carrying harness are already adjusted for the wearer's personal use; also that the warning device, lamp etc. is functioning correctly and that the completed breathing apparatus tally and personal line are attached.

Donning and start-up   Drill M5

(a) Self-Contained Compressed Air Sets

(i)   Don the apparatus pack fashion, placing the face mask neck strap (or cord) over the head, and adjust the shoulder straps to support the set comfortably on the back. (Where a neck strap is not fitted, a tether will hold the face mask in a safe position.)

(ii)   Fasten the waist belt comfortably tight and secure the chest strap (if fitted).

(iii) Check that the positive pressure switch (if fitted) is in the positive pressure *'off'* position; check that the fresh air valve (if fitted) is in the *'open'* position.

(iv) Open the cylinder valve fully and check that the warning whistle sounds momentarily.

(v) Read the pressure gauge and check that the cylinder contains not less than 80 per cent of its maximum capacity.

(vi) Fit the face mask and adjust the head straps. Close fresh air valve (if fitted).

(vii) Turn the positive pressure switch (if fitted) to the positive pressure *'on'* position.

(viii) Insert finger at side of face mask momentarily to release seal and check that the air continues to flow thus ensuring positive pressure operation.

(ix) Return the positive pressure switch (if fitted) to the *'off'* position.

(x) Check for gas tightness in accordance with the manufacturers instructions.

(xi) Return the positive pressure switch (if fitted) to the *'on'* position.

(xii) Check tally and safety lamp.

(xiii) Report drill complete to BA control officer.

Note: In the case of a positive pressure set which is not provided with a positive pressure switch there will be a considerable loss of air if the main valve is opened before the facemask if fitted to the face. In these circumstances the face mask should be fitted temporarily and the main valve fully opened before making the final adjustment to the facemask.

(b) Air-line Apparatus (Air-line Supervisor and Two Wearers)

(i) *Wearers.* Don and secure the harness, adjust to a comfortable fit.

(ii) Support the facemask using the strap or cord. Check that the positive pressure switch (if fitted) is in the positive pressure *'off'* position; check that the fresh air valve (if fitted) is in the *'open'* position.

(iii) *Air-line Supervisor.* Open No. 2 Cylinder valve, read the pressure gauge and check that the cylinder contains not less than 80 per cent of its maximum capacity. Close the cylinder valve and check that the warning whistle unit operates at the correct pressure.

(iv)   Release the air from the apparatus, then close the air release valve.

(v)   Open No. 1 Cylinder valve, read the pressure gauge and check the contents of the cylinder as above.

(vi)   *Wearers.* Fit the facemask and adjust the headstraps. Close the fresh air valve (if fitted).

(vii) Turn the positive pressure switch (if fitted) to the positive pressure *'on'* position.

(viii) Insert finger at side of facemask, momentarily, to release seal and check that the air continues to flow thus ensuring positive pressure operation.

(ix)   Return the positive pressure switch to the *"off"* position.

(x)   *Air-line Supervisor/Wearers.* Check for gas tightness in accordance with the manufacturers instructions.

(xi)   For air lines incorporating a communication cable with the air hose the opportunity should be taken at this stage to test the communications equipment in accordance with the test prescribed on Page 173.

Notes on the use of fireboats

Owing to the small number of brigades which man fireboats, and the wide diversity in design and use, it is not considered to be appropriate to include specific fireboat drills in this publication. However, brigades will have devised drills to meet their local needs, in these circumstances the following points should be borne in mind.

1. Before commencement of a drill all personnel should be numbered and suitably positioned on the fireboat in the safest and most convenient location. In addition, it is essential that each member of the crew is conversant not only with his own duties but also with those of the other members of the crew with whom he is working. Consequently, although it may be impossible to effect a change round in the orthodox manner, the importance of arranging for each man to perform the duties of the other members of the crew must not be overlooked.

2. The officer in charge of a fireboat is responsible for the safety of both the vessel and the crew and he should ensure that the crew wear lifejackets when necessary.

3. The coxswain is responsible for navigation and he must be aware that navigational safety of the vessel has priority when working under the operational direction of the officer in charge.

4. When hose is taken ashore to land appliances, land crews should lay hose from the water's edge with couplings a foot or so above the water level, and should make hose lines fast by means of a line if working from a quay or high bank.

5. Some of the more important terms which are used on fireboats are illustrated opposite.

6. The value of frequent combined drills/exercises using fireboat and land crews should not be underestimated.

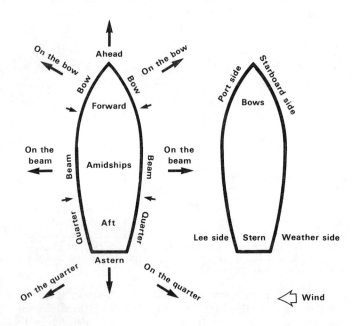

Standard abbreviations

Note: These abbreviations should not be used over the telephone or radio.

1. Appliances

BAT	Breathing Apparatus Tender
BACV	Breathing Apparatus Control Van
BL	Breakdown Lorry
CIU	Chemical Incident Unit
CU	Control Unit
DECON. U.	Decontamination Unit
EST	Combined Emergency Tender and Salvage Tender
ET	Emergency Tender
FBt	Fireboat
FoT	Foam Tender
FST	Foam Salvage Tender
HL	Hose Layer
HP	Hydraulic Platform
HPP	Hydraulic Platform with Booster Pump fitted
P	Pump with 9m or 10.5m Extension Ladder
PE	Pump Escape
PL	Pump with 13.5m Extension Ladder
PST	Pump Salvage Tender
ST	Salvage Tender
TL	Turntable Ladder
WC	Staff Car with Wireless
WrE	Water Tender Escape
WrL	Water Tender with 13.5m Extension Ladder
WrT	Water Tender with 9m or 10.5m Extension ladder.

2. Ancillary appliances

Amb	Ambulance
CaV	Canteen Vehicle
FTr	Foam Trailer
GPL	General Purpose Lorry
L4P	Light Four-Wheel-Drive Vehicle fitted with pump
L4R	Light Four-wheel-Drive Vehicle with rescue equipment
L4T	Light Four-wheel-Drive Vehicle fitted with Hose Reel
L4V	Light Four-wheel-Drive Vehicle
LU	Lighting Unit
LUTr	Lighting Unit Trailer
MW	Mobile Workshop

PCV	Personnel Carrying Vehicle
STr	Salvage Trailer
SV	Service Vehicle
WrC	Water Carrier.

3. Equipment

ALU	Air Lifting Unit
BA	Breathing Apparatus
ELG	Emergency Lifting Gear
FBP	Foam Branch Pipe
FG	Foam (Mechanical) Generator
HR	Hose Reel
HX	High Expansion Foam
LX	Low Expansion foam
LPP	Light Portable Pump (below 1600 litres per min.)

4. Personnel

CFO	Chief Fire Officer
DCO	Deputy Chief Officer
ACO	Assistant Chief Officer
SDO	Senior Divisional Officer
DC	Divisional Commander
DDC	Deputy Divisional Commander
DO	Divisional Officer
PFCO	Principal Fire Control Officer
ADO	Assistant Divisional Officer
GFCO	Group Fire Control Officer
Stn O	Station Officer
FCO	Fire Control Officer
FIT	Fire Investigation Team
Sub O	Sub Officer
SFCOp	Senior Fire Control Operator
LFm	Leading fireman
LFw	Leading Firewoman
LFCOp	Leading Fire Control Operator
FCOp	Fire Control Operator
Fm	Fireman
Fw	Firewoman
JFm	Junior Fireman
JFw	Junior Firewoman
Oic	Officer in Charge
Com O	Communications Officer
FPO	Fire Prevention Officer
Mob O	Mobilising Officer
SSO	Senior Staff Officer
SO	Staff Officer

TMO	Transport Maintenance Officer
WO	Water Officer

5. Premises

Bde	Brigade
Bde con	Control at Brigade headquarters
Cmd	Command
Con	Control
Div	Division/Divisional
Div Con	Control at Divisional Headquarters
Div HQ	Divisional Headquarters
HQ	Headquarters, combining administrative offices and control
HQ Admin	Headquarters, administrative offices only
Stn	Station
WS	Workshops

6. Miscellaneous

Actg	Acting
AFA	Automatic Fire Alarm
AFD	Automatic Fire Detection
CD	Civil Defence
CFBAC	Central Fire Brigades Advisory Council
DM	Day Manning
Ex Tel	Exchange Telephone
FP	Fire prevention
FSEB	Fire Services Examination Board
Hr	Hour
JCAEU	Jont Committee on Appliances, Equipment and Uniform
JCFBC	Joint Committee on Fire Brigade Communications
JCFBO	Joint Committee on Fire Brigade Operations
JCFR	Joint Committee on Fire Research
JFPC	Joint Fire Prevention Committee
JPC	Joint Pensions Committee
JTC	Joint Training Committee
Nuc	Nucleus
OOO	Out of Order
PC	Police Constable
PCB	Public Call Box
Pol	Police
RCT	Running Call Telephone
Ret	Retained
Rly	Railway
RT	Radio Telephone
Tel	Telephone

Temp	Temporary
Vol	Volunteer
WFB	Works Fire Brigade
WT	Whole-time

Additional abreviations applicable to Scotland

Fmr	Firemaster
DFmr	Deputy Firemaster
AFmr	Assistant Firemaster
SCFBAC	Scottish Central Fire Brigades Advisory Council

Glossary of terms used in the Fire Service

A. Appliances and equipment

Adaptors:
   Delivery hose adaptor. A fitting used for connecting together two lengths of hose with different types of couplings.

   Suction hose adaptor. A fitting used to connect suction hose to delivery hose or to suction hose of a different diameter.

'Air bags'.
   (Air Lifting Units) Reinforced inflatable cushions used for lifting when the use of conventional mechanical jacks is impracticable. Operated by compressed air via control valves.

Applicator
   An extension tube to carry a spray nozzle to enable an operator to apply the spray to otherwise inaccessible places.

Aqueous film forming foam (AFFF)
   (See light water foam)

Axes:
   Large axe. Sometimes know as a 'felling axe' used for breaking in or for cutting away heavy timber, etc.

   Fireman's axe. A small axe used for cutting away.

Blank cap
   A cover fitted to delivery, inlet and suction connections when not in use. Also used to protect threads on other equipment, e.g. on BA cylinders.

Branches:
   Branch. A tapering fitting employed at the end of a line of hose between the delivery coupling and the nozzle, in order to increase the velocity of the water and so assist the nozzle to provide a solid jet.

   Diffuser branch. A branch which can give a spray or a jet of variable size and which can be shut off at will.

   Foam making branch-pipe. A branch used for generating and discharge of mechanical foam in which the foam solution is aerated, expanded and discharged as a jet or spray.

   Foam branch. A similar device to a foam making branchpipe, except that it does not induce the air.

Hand-controlled branch. A branch with the capability to stop or reduce the flow of water. It may be capable of delivering a jet or spray or both simultaneously.

Streamform branch. A short branch with an internal central tube and guide vanes to reduce turbulence in the water.

Breathing Apparatus

Apparatus which is provided with its own supply of oxygen or compressed air, designed to enable the wearer to breathe safely in irrespirable atmospheres.

Breechings:

Collecting breeching. A fitting used to join two lines of hose to form one.

Dividing breeching. A fitting used to divide one line of hose into two.

Note: A breeching fitted with a valve to control the flow of water is known as a 'controlled dividing breeching' or a 'controlled collecting breeching'.

Ceiling hook

A long wooden pole having, at one end, a steel point with a spur at right angles.

Chemical Incident Unit

An appliance designed to attend chemical incidents. The special equipment carried includes protective suits, compressed air breathing apparatus, radiation monitoring equipment, a 110 volt DC generator for providing lighting and the operation of vacuum cleaners (incorporating dust filters) used in dry decontamination procedures.

Chemical protection suit.

A rubber or plastic suit which, in conjunction with self contained breathing apparatus, gloves and boots, affords protection to the skin from damage by aggressive solids or liquids through spillage or splash.

Chimney rods

Jointed rods to which the tubing of a stirrup pump can be connected for dealing with chimney fires.

Collecting head

Or 'suction collecting head'. Used to connect one or more lines of hose to the suction inlet of a pump.

Collector pumping
A method of increasing water supplies by stationing pumps at a number of sources and delivering water to the collecting head of a single pump from which it is pumped on to the fire.

Control Unit
A vehicle equipped as a mobile control room for use by the officer commanding at large fires. Usually equipped with radio and sometimes with field telephones. Normally identified by red and white chequered markings.

Contamination Meter
An instrument used to detect contamination by radioactive particles; usually measures in counts per second.

Couplings:
Delivery hose. An instantaneous coupling—there is one standard size (62.5 mm) for all sizes of delivery hose.

Suction hose. A round-thread screwed coupling, the standard sizes being for 75mm, 100mm and 140mm bore hose.

Crowbar
Usually has a chisel edge at one end and a claw at the other.

Dam
A container, usually portable, to hold water from which pumps can be got to work.

Delivery head
A fitting used principally on fireboats by which water from the pump or pumps is made to feed a number of hose lines simultaneously. Each outlet is controlled by a valve.

Distress signal unit
A hand-operated device fitted to the harness of breathing apparatus to enable a distress warning signal to be sounded when necessary.

Door breaker
A device for breaking in a door, or forcing it off its hinges, in order to effect an entry.

Dosemeter
An instrument that records the total amount of gamma radiation received by the wearer.

Ejector pump

A portable jet pump designed for removing water from depths beyond the maximum practical lift of pumps and/or in confined spaces. It can be used in basements, ships holds, etc. It is operated by water delivered from a pump through standard delivery hose.

Emergency Tender

An appliance carrying specialised equipment, such as cutting and lighting equipment, breathing and resuscitation apparatus, etc.

Fire beater

A wooden shaft, usually at one end of which is fitted a piece of reinforced canvas. Used for beating out heath and grass fires.

Fireboat

A motor vessel, usually twin-screw, with pumps designed for fire fighting.

Fire Extinguishers:

CO$_2$ fire extinguishers. A fire extinguisher containing liquid carbon dioxide (CO$_2$) which is released as a gas on the actuation of the extinguisher.

Dry powder fire extinguisher (gas cartridge). A fire extinguisher containing dry powder which is expelled by pressure from a cartridge of compressed gas attached to or fitted into the extinguisher.

Dry powder fire extinguisher (stored pressure). A fire extinguisher containing dry powder which is expelled by pressure stored within the body of the extinguisher as a whole.

Foam fire extinguisher (chemical). A fire extinguisher from which chemical foam is expelled when the chemical solutions, stored separately within the body of the extinguisher, are allowed to mix and react.

Foam fire extinguisher (mechanical, gas cartridge). A fire extinguisher from which mechanical foam is expelled by pressure from a cartridge of compressed gas attached to or fitted into the extinguisher.

Foam fire extinguisher (mechanical—stored pressure). A fire extinguisher from which mechanical foam is expelled by pressure stored within the body of the extinguisher as a whole.

Vaporising liquid fire extinguisher (gas cartridge). A fire extinguisher containing a vaporising liquid which is expelled by pressure from a cartridge of compressed gas attached to or fitted into the extinguisher.

Vaporising liquid fire extinguisher (stored pressure). A fire extinguisher containing a vaporising liquid which is expelled by pressure stored within the body of the extinguisher as a whole.

Water fire extinguisher (gas cartridge). A fire extinguisher in which the water is expelled by pressure from a cartridge of compressed gas attached to or fitted into the extinguisher.

Water fire extinguisher (soda acid). A fire extinguisher from which the medium is expelled by gas pressure from an acid/alkali reaction in the contents of the extinguisher.

Water fire extinguisher (stored pressure). A fire extinguisher from which water is expelled by pressure stored within the body of the extinguisher as a whole.

Fireground
The area in which and on which fire-fighting operations are in progress.

Fire hydrant
A fitting attached to a water main below street or pavement level. The hydrant incorporates a control valve and an outlet connection to which a standpipe can be attached. ('Double' hydrants have two control valves and two outlets).

Fire hydrant cover key
A tool used to lift the cover of certain types of hydrant.

Fire hydrant key and bar
A tool used to open up a hydrant and to turn on the valve.

Fire hydrant pit
The recess below the road or pavement level in which a hydrant is located.

First-aid box
The medical first-aid box carried on appliances.

Foam
The product of a mixture of foam concentrate, water and air.

Foam concentrate
A liquid used in the production of mechanical foam.

Foam container:
A container to carry foam concentrate.

Foam dam:
A portable reservoir to provide a continuous supply of foam concentrate for pick-up tubes.

Foam Generator (High Expansion)
See 'High Expansion Foam Generator'.

Foam (mechanical) Generator
A device introduced into a line of hose for creating mechanical foam, which is discharged through a branch.

Foam inlet adaptor
An adaptor fitted on fixed foam inlets to enable foam branch pipes to feed into a fixed installation.

Foam inductor
A piece of equipment whereby the correct quantity of foam concentrate is induced into a water stream.

Foam solution
A solution of foam concentrate in water at an appropriate concentration.

Foam Tender
An appliance wholly or mainly used for carrying foam-producing equipment.

Gantry
A fitting at the rear of an appliance to carry a ladder.

Gas tight chemical protection suit
A rubber or plastic suit fitted with an integral face mask which, in conjunction with compressed air breathing apparatus, offers protection from absorbtion via inhalation, ingestion and absorbtion through the skin and from dermal damage.

Gloves (Electrical protection)
Gloves for use where live electrical wires or apparatus are involved.

Headrest
Fitting located at the front of a pump escape, turntable ladder, pump, etc. to take the weight of the head of the ladder.

Hearth kit
A kit of tools required for dealing with hearth fires and cutting away, includes floorboard saw, cold and bolster chisels, club hammer, hacksaw, etc.

High Expansion Foam Generator

A piece of equipment for generating high expansion foam. It consists essentially of a fan which derives a spray of water and foam solution through a net gauze. The foam thus formed is delivered through a short trunking of large cross-sectional area as it can only operate a relatively small back pressure.

Hose:

Delivery hose. Hose used on the delivery side of a pump the standard sizes are 45mm, 70mm, and 90mm.

Suction hose. Hose specially constructed to withstand external pressure. For use on the suction side of a pump. Normally referred to simply as 'suction'. The standard sizes are 75mm, 100mm, 140mm bore.

Hose becket/sling

A rope or webbing sling used for securing hose on a ladder, those used on turntable ladders are often made of leather.

Hose ramp

A device to enable vehicles to pass over delivery hose without damage to the hose.

Hose Reel Equipment

Carried on fire appliances and used to deal with small fires. Water is carried in a tank on a vehicle and pumped at high and/or low pressures through 20mm bore rubber hose which is carried on a revolving reel from which only the required length need be drawn off, small diameter nozzles or fog guns may be attached to the end of the hose.

Hose strap

A strap used for securing a length of hose when it is rolled.

Hydraulic Platform

An appliance consisting of two hydraulically-operated booms with a cage at the upper end. The larger sizes may also have a hydraulically-operated arm provided to extend the length of the upper boom. Appliances range in size from a maximum height of 13.7m to 30.5m. The booms can be operated from the cage or from the turntable and can be rotated through 360 degrees. The cage is fitted with a monitor for use as a water tower, and can also be used for rescue purposes.

Ladders:

Extension Ladder (9m or 10.5m). A two-section ladder, extended by means of a line.

Extension Ladder (13.5m with props). A three-section ladder with jacks, plumbing gear, and supporting props, and extended by means of a line.

Short Extension Ladder. A light ladder in two sections extending to approx. 4 metres.

Triple Extension Ladder. A light ladder of three sections of push up type extending between 5.6 and 6m.

Light water foam

An extinguishing medium having the ability to assist water to float on the surface of flammable liquids and provide a seal to prevent reignition.

Lighten hose:

Assist to take the weight of a hose.

Lines:

Belt line. See 'Pocket Line'.

Bobbin line. A line wound on to a bobbin and carried in a pouch on some types of safety belt. Used for hauling up small gear. May also be used as a guy line or as a guide line.

Escape line. A line between 4.5m and 6m length secured to the top round of an escape or extension ladder to assist men to find their way back from a smoke laden room. It may also be used to secure the head of an extension ladder.

Grass line. A line made of coir or man made fibre which will float on water.

Ground control line. A line used to control a turntable ladder monitor from ground level.

Guide line. A line 61m long used in certain circumstances to guide men in and out of a building when breathing apparatus is worn.

Guy line. (i) A line (usually 40m long) attached to a turntable ladder to assist in maintaining stability in a high wind. (ii) A line bent on to an object (e.g. rescue sling, stretcher or ladder) to keep it clear of obstructions whilst being lowered.

Long line. A 16mm diameter manila line, 30m long.

Lowering line. A 16mm diameter polyester line 40m long, may have two legs one of which is spliced in 1.5m from one end of the line. Each leg is fitted with a running eye.

Personal line. A line up to 6m long, secured at one end to a B.A. set and fitted at the other end with a snap hook for attaching to a guide line when breathing apparatus is worn. This line may be used at its full extent (6m) for searching off a guide line or it may be used 'short' (1.25m) for traversing a guide line.

Pocket line. A small diameter line carried in the fire tunic pocket and used for lashing branches etc.

Rescue line. A special 16mm diameter polyester line (usually 70m long) used for rescue work with turntable ladders.

Short line. A 16mm diameter manila line, 15m long.

Tail line. A line not more than 6m long permanently attached to a turntable ladder rescue sling. Used to prevent undue swing of a person being rescued when the turntable ladder is trained away from a building.

Line/round protector
A device, preferably made of a suitable aluminium alloy, designed to fit over the rounds of all types of ladder and to readily be attached to whichever round it is desired to use in order to protect the lowering line and round from damage when carrying out lowering drills.

Monitor
A special type of branch with lateral and vertical travel mounted on an appliance, or one designed to operate unattended at ground level when it is known as 'ground monitor'.

Nozzles:
Plain nozzle. The piece of equipment which screws on to the end of the branch and which determines the size of the jet.

Spray nozzle. A nozzle designed to discharge water in the form of a spray.

Nozzle spanner
A spanner used to tighten the joint between nozzle and branch.

Padlock remover
A lever fitted with slots into which a padlock is inserted. It is used to twist off a padlock when effecting an entry.

Persuader
A cigar-shaped cold chisel mounted in a holder and used in conjunction with a sledge hammer to force the hasp of a padlock.

Pick-up tube
A tube through which foam concentrate is drawn into foam-making equipment.

Portable Pump

A self-contained portable fire-fighting pumping unit.

Pumps (General)

Either self-propelled, portable, stirrup or ejector. (See separate entries).

Pump (Appliance)

A self propelled appliance having a built-in pump with a minimum capacity of 2270 1/min. Carries a 10.5m extension ladder and hose reel equipment with a minimum tank capacity of 364 litres of water.

Pump escape

A pump (appliance) with a hose reel tank capacity of at least 455 litres and carrying a wheeled escape.

Pump ladder

A pump (appliance) with a hose reel tank capacity of 455 litres and carrying a 13.5 ladder.

Rescue sling

A special sling used for lowering persons. It has two loops connected to a steel ring by which it is attached to a turntable ladder rescue line. Sometimes used an an alternative to spliced legs on a lowering line.

Resuscitation Apparatus

Apparatus for supplying oxygen or a mixture of oxygen and air to a person needing artificial respiration.

Safety belt—'Turntable ladder'

A special belt with a swivel type hook for use with turntable ladders.

Safety device

A mechanical device incorporating a line and belt. The device must be attached to the head of the turntable ladder or hydraulic platform or to the anchorage of a drill tower.

Safety device belt

The belt, attached to the line of a safety device, which must be worn by the man being carried down.

Salvage Tender

An appliance wholly or mainly used for carrying specialised equipment such as waterproof sheets, sawdust, etc. to prevent or minimise water damage.

Slipper strainer

A low level suction strainer, water can only enter via the bottom of the strainer which stands on four squat legs, facilitating pumping from shallow water.

Standpipe

Used on a hydrant to bring the outlet above the ground level. The term ordinarily includes the bend at the top which when used separately is known as the standpipe head. Standpipes may have one or two outlets and are then known as single or double outlet respectively.

Steel-shod lever

A large wooden lever steel shod for lifting heavy objects and forcing doors, etc.

Stirrup pump

A small pump used in conjunction with a bucket of water, worked by hand and held steady by a foot stirrup, fitted with 12.5mm rubber tubing with 3mm nozzle and delivers up to 5.5 1/min.

Strainers:

Basket strainer. Used over the suction strainer to prevent the entry of dirt and leaves, etc. The canvas part is known as the 'skirt'.

Conical strainer. A removable wire strainer fitted in the suction inlet of a pump.

Suction strainer. A metal strainer, connected to the end of suction hose, to prevent the entry into the suction of objects liable to choke or damage the pump.

Suction:

Hard suction. Suction hose designed to withstand both internal and external pressure. It is used between open water supplies and the pump.

Soft suction. Delivery type hose used to connect a pump to a pressure fed source of water.

Suction wrench.

Used to tighten suction couplings.

Survey meter

An instrument used to detect and measure gamma radiation; also known as a 'dose-rate meter.'

Turntable Ladder

A sectional ladder mounted on a self-propelled chassis which can be extended to about 30m. It is operated hydraulically and can be rotated through a complete circle. It is usually fitted with a monitor at the head of the ladder.

Water tender

A self propelled appliance having a built in pump with a minimum capacity of 2270 1/min. Carries a 10.5m extension ladder and hose reel equipment with a water tank capacity of not less than 1820 litres or more than 2270 litres. A portable fire-fighting pump may also be carried.

Water tender escape

A water tender carrying a wheeled escape.

A water tender ladder

A water tender carrying a 13.5m ladder.

Wheeled escape

A wheeled extending ladder, usually mounted on a fire appliance from which it can be removed and manoeuvred into position for rescue or fire-fighting purposes.

B. Telecommunication terms

1. General

Acceptance point
A place where fire calls are received.

Central commercial alarm centre
A point where automatic fire alarms, fire telephones, intruder alarms etc., from protected buildings may terminate. The centre accepts the responsibility for passing on calls to the appropriate emergency service control.

Control room
A permanently manned and fully equipped room in fire service premises in which emergency calls are received and subsequent action is taken to mobilise personnel, appliances and equipment.

'Distress call'
A priority call over the public telephone system for sending urgent operational fire messages. (Used only to obtain rapid connection in cases involving the safety of life or property; the caller's request to the Post Office operator being prefixed by the phrase: 'Distress call').

Fire alarm call point manual
A device for the manual operation of an electrical fire alarm system.

Fire alarm system, manual
A fire alarm system in which the alarm is initiated manually.

Fire alarm system, automatic
A fire alarm system comprising components for automatically detecting a fire, initiating an alarm of fire and initiating other action as arranged, the system may also include manual call points.

Fire telephone.
A telephone provided exclusively for summoning the fire brigade; often connected to a private circuit from a fire risk to a fire station, central control room or central commercial alarm centre.

Priority signalling facility.
A facility for transmitting an urgent calling signal to the distant end of circuit.

Private wire circuit.

A dedicated telephone circuit permanently connected between two or more points for transmission and reception of speech and/or data.

Public switched telephone network (PSTN).

A switching system which allows public access to anyone connected to the national and international telephone network.

PSTN standby line.

Secondary means of operating a call-out system by dialled-up connection on PSTN.

Subscriber trunk dialling (STD).

A facility to dial direct, without operator assistance, any other subscriber on the national network.

Teleprinter.

An electro-mechanical device resembling a typewriter which, by electrical impulses transmitted over a line or radio link, remotely operates a suitable machine at the receiving point or points.

2. Call-out systems

Acknowledgement signal

A signal transmitted back solely as a result of the reception of another signal, e.g., a signal received at the call-out point of a remote control system indicating that remote equipment has operated. It may not, however, indicate that other alerting systems linked to the remote equipment are in fact operating.

Call-out installation

A line installation or radio alerter system, with associated control equipment used to summon firemen to the fire station from their homes and/or places of employment.

Call-out point

The place from which a call-out installation is remotely controlled.

Identification signal

A signal received at the call-out point of a remote control system indicating that connection has been made with remote equipment. It does not indicate that the remote equipment is operating.

Paging system

A selective call, personal paging system which may utilise the outgoing transmit frequency of a fire brigade main radio scheme, an independent paging facility using its own unique frequency, or the telecommunications paging network.

Paging encoder
The control equipment of a paging system, usually located in the central control room.

Public address system
A loudspeaker system which may be operated by remote control from a central control room or locally for both operational and administrative purposes.

Running-call facility
A facility at a fire station which enables a running caller to give an alarm of fire.

3. Radio

Double-frequency scheme
A scheme using one frequency for main station transmissions and out-station reception, and another frequency for out-station transmissions and main station reception.

Duplex working
A communications technique in which it is possible to transmit and receive simultaneously; e.g., as in ordinary telephone conversation.

General clearance
A radio operating procedure term used by main control operators to denote that a period of traffic is completed and that out-stations may call-in as necessary; e.g., '....M2XY Out'.

Main control
The place where main control operators and equipment are situated and from where the radio traffic of a scheme is controlled. A main control may be remote from a main station.

Main station
The place where the main transmitting and receiving equipment of a scheme is located. Sometimes, it also includes the main control equipment and operators.

Multi-station scheme
A scheme served by several main stations (e.g., a large county scheme).

Out-stations
All radio stations in a scheme, including two-way fixed and mobile sets, and fixed receivers, but excluding main stations, main and sub-controls.

Hand-held set
A hand-held low-powered portable radio transmitter/receiver.

Pocket Alerter System
A call-out system utilising radio pocket alerters carried by certain firemen which are triggered by a radio signal transmitted by a remotely-controlled alerter transmitter usually located at the fire station.

Pocket Alerter
A small alerter receiver carried by a fireman when he is on call and which sounds either an 'alert' or 'test' signal when actuated by a radio signal from the alerter transmitter.

Pocket Alerter Transmitter
A transmitter, usually located at a fire station and remotely controlled from a central control room. It transmits either a 'fire' or 'test' signal to pocket alerters and operates from float-charged batteries.

Simplex working
A communication technique in which it is not possible to transmit and receive simultaneously; e.g., as in a radio scheme where 'Over' procedure is necessary.

Single-frequency scheme
A scheme using one common frequency for transmitting and receiving by all stations.

Single-stations scheme
A small scheme served by one main station.

Sub-control
A point from which temporary control of a scheme can be exercised, but only with the co-operation of main control operators.

Transportable set
A portable transmitter/receiver of roughly the same power as a mobile set. Normally used on the loss of main station facilities, or to enhance the power of hand held sets to cover a wider area.

'Talk-through'
A facility on double-frequency radio schemes which interconnects incoming and outgoing channels. Used to enable out-stations on a scheme to hear and talk to each other.

VHF/UHF Mobile Repeater Unit
A composite mobile radio installation comprising a VHF transmitter/receiver (on main scheme channels) interfaced with a UHF transmitter/receiver (on hand held set channels). Can operate either:
- (a) On main scheme channel
- (b) On hand held set channel (with talk-through) to enhance range of hand held sets
- (c) Hand held set through to main scheme stations direct.

4. Computer Systems

Acoustic coupler
A device that permits the transmission of data over telephone circuits without making a hardwire (fixed) electrical connection to the line.

Bit
An abbreviation for binary digit which is the unit of information, presented as either a '0' or a '1'.

Byte
A sequence of binary digits contained as a unit.

Cell
A storage space in a computer memory for one item of data.

Central processing unit (CPU)
The unit of a computer in which processing of data takes place.

Chemdata
Microcomputer based chemical information retrieval system.

Computer
A machine, controlled by a stored programme, which automatically inputs and processes data and outputs the results of processing.

Data Processing (DP)
Storing, retrieving, sorting or selecting data, changing data

from one form to another, doing calculations or making decisions based on data.

Data Transmission

The movement of information in coded form over a transmission system by breaking down letters and figures into codes in order to send messages by electronic means.

Hard Copy

A permanent record obtained on paper through a printer.

Hardware

The physical units of equipment which make up a computer.

Line Printer

An output device which prints out one complete line of information at a time.

Modem

A device for converting digital information into voice frequency signals for transmission over a speech network or for converting signals back again into digital form at the receiving end of the circuit.

Peripheral

A piece of equipment linked to a computer.

Program

A set of instructions to a computer.

Software

An alternative term to Program.

Terminal

A device providing a direct link between a computer and the person using it.

Visual Display Unit (VDU)

A terminal where data is displayed on a screen rather like a television screen.

BADGES OF RANK IN THE FIRE SERVICE

In the Fire Service the different ranks can be identified by badges on the shoulders, cap and helmet.

Note: In order to obtain a clear visual distinction between yellow and white helmets under all lighting conditions, the combs of all white helmets should be painted black.

Rank	Shoulder markings for Undress Uniforms	
Chief Officer/ Firemaster	Large impeller within laurel wreath with two small impellers above. Arranged one above the other.	
Chief Officer	Also, on each lapel of the undress uniform a gorget patch of black with a centre cord of red oak leaves.	
Firemaster	Also, on each lapel of the undress uniform a gorget patch of black with thistle design in silver.	
Assistant Chief Officer/ Assistant firemaster	Large impeller within laurel wreath with one small impeller above.	
	Also, on each lapel of the undress uniform a gorget patch of black with a centre strip of one row of red tracing.	
Senior Divisional Officer	Horizontal chromium bar, 3mm wide, below large impeller within laurel wreath	

Cap markings	Helmet markings	
Two rows of silver oak leaves on peak	One black band 38mm wide on a white helmet with a black comb	
Two rows of silver thistles on peak		
Assistant Chief Officer	Two black bands each 19mm wide, with 12.5mm separation on a white helmet with a black comb	
One row of silver oak leaves on peak		
Assistant Firemaster		
One row of silver thistles on peak		
One 12.5mm band of silver braid on peak	One black band 19mm wide, surmounted by one black band 12.5mm wide, with 12.5mm separation on a white helmet with a black comb	

Rank	Shoulder markings for Undress Uniforms	
Divisional Officer I, II and III	Large impeller within laurel wreath	
Principal Fire Control Officer	Small impeller within small laurel wreath	
Assistant Divisional Officer	Three large impellers arranged one above the other	
Group Fire Control Officer	Three small impellers arranged one above the other	
Station Officer	Two large impellers arranged one above the other	

Cap markings	Helmet markings	
One 12.5mm band of silver braid on peak	One black band 19mm wide, surmounted by one black band 12.5mm wide, with 12.5mm separation on a white helmet with a black comb	
As for Divisional Officer		
Plain cloth peak	One black band 19mm wide, on a white helmet with a black comb	
Plain brim or cloth peak		
Plain cloth peak	One black band 12.5mm wide, on a white helmet with black comb	

Rank	Shoulder markings for Undress Uniforms	
Fire Control Officer	Two small impellers arranged one above the other	
Sub-Officer	Two horizontal chrome bars. 12.5mm wide	
Senior Fire Control Operator	Two horizontal chrome bars, 6mm wide	
Leading Fireman/ Leading Firewoman	Horizontal chrome bar, 12.5mm wide	
Leading Fire Control Operator	Horizontal chrome bar, 6mm wide	

Cap markings	Helmet markings
Plain brim or cloth peak	
Standard pattern cap or hat	Two black bands each 12.5mm wide, with 12.5mm wide separation on a yellow helmet 
Standard pattern cap or hat	
Standard pattern cap or hat	One black band 12.5mm wide on a yellow helmet
Standard pattern cap or hat	

Standard tests and examinations
for Fire Service equipment

The officer in charge of a station is responsible for the general efficiency of his station, including the appliances and equipment, and it is part of his duties to see that these are regularly tested and examined.

The tests and examinations set out below are for general guidance and the results should be recorded as necessary in accordance with brigade practice.

A guide to the frequency of tests or examinations is given in the Standard Test Table which is designed to provide a ready reference indicating the intervals at which some form of check, test or technical inspection is required. The intervals between tests and examinations are regarded as maxima and may be applied more frequently where equipment is used extensively. Reference throughout to testing or examination 'on acceptance at station' means on receipt of new or transferred appliances or equipment at the station and the term after 'operational use' means use at fires or other incidents.

Any defects revealed by the test or examination should be dealt with immediately, either by rectifying the fault or by reporting through the appropriate channels.

The general aim of tests and examinations should be to ensure that the appliances and every piece of equipment carried on an appliance is in efficient working order. It is the duty of officers in charge of stations to ensure that any unusual or special apparatus for which no tests are specified and which is carried on their appliances is adequately tested at sufficient intervals to ensure its correct operation when required.

In a number of tests which follow, reference is made to the weight of one or more men. The weight of one man carrying out such tests should be close to but not exceeding 76 kg, similarly where the weight of more than one man is employed, the average should not exceed 76 kg. Under no circumstances should the weight of more men than are specified be employed. Except in the case of jumping rounds, the weight of men should be applied without shock.

Standard Test Table

This Standard Test Table is intended only as a guide to the frequency at which some form of check, test or technical inspection is required. It is important that reference is made to the specific test for precise details

		On acceptance at station
Pumps	Self propelled and portable	✓
Stirrup pumps		✓
Hose	Delivery and Hose reel	✓
	Suction	✓
Hose reel equipment		✓
Nozzles and Branches		✓
Escapes		✓
Ladders	13.5m	✓
	Extension: 9m, 10.5m, three section short and short	✓
Turntable		✓
Hydraulic Platforms		✓
Wire Ropes		
Belts	Hook, Safety, Rescue Slings, Harnesses and Stretchers	✓
Lines	Rescue, lowering and Escape	✓
	Guy, BA Guide and personal lines	✓
	Long and Short lines	✓
Everest Device and Anchorages		✓
Breathing Apparatus		✓

Note: Cylinder Hydraulic Test — 3 or 5 yearly as appropriate

Before drills	After operational use or drill	Daily	Weekly	Monthly	3 Monthly	6 Monthly	12 Monthly	Page
				✓				
	✓			✓				
	✓						✓	
	✓			✓				
				✓				
						✓		
	✓			✓			✓	
	✓			✓			✓	
	✓			✓				
	✓			✓	✓			
	✓			✓	✓		✓	
As and when appropriate appliances and equipment are tested								
✓	✓			✓				
✓	✓			✓				
	✓			✓				
	✓			✓				
✓				✓	✓			
	✓	✓	✓					

	On acceptance at station
BA Ancillary Equipment *Note:* In addition, test after battery replacement	✔
Resuscitation Apparatus *Note:* Cylinder Hydraulic Test — 5 yearly	✔
Extinguishers Examination or inspection	
Water (soda acid) type	✔
Water (gas cartridge) type	✔
Water (stored pressure) type (external)	✔
Foam (chemical type)	✔
Foam (mechanical) (gas cartridge) type	✔
Foam (mechanical) (stored pressure) type	✔
Foam (mechanical) (stored pressure) type (external)	✔
*Carbon dioxide type	✔
*Vaporising liquid (Halon) (stored pressure) type	✔
*Dry Powder (gas cartridge) type	✔
*Dry Powder (stored pressure) type	✔
Extinguishers Discharge test	

Note: All above extinguishers with exception of those marked* are discharge

Carbon dioxide

Vaporising liquid (Halon)
(stored pressure or dissolved pressure) type 'A' and 'B'

Dry powder (gas cartridge) type
Dry powder (stored pressure) type — factory sealed
                                 — field refillable

Before drills	After operational use or drill	Daily	Weekly	Monthly	3 Monthly	6 Monthly	12 Monthly	Page
	✓			✓				
	✓		✓					
					✓			
					✓			
					✓			
					✓			
					✓			
					✓			
					✓			
					✓			
					✓			
					✓			
					✓			
								(See note)

tested annually. The remainder are as follows:

Discharge tested after 10 years and 20 years
from acceptance, (thereafter) 5 years

Discharge tested at intervals not exeeding 5 years
from the date of last discharge whether at a fire or test purpose

Discharge tested at intervals of 2 years
Discharge tested at intervals of 4 years
Discharge tested at intervals of 2 years

	On acceptance at station
Rubber Gloves *Note:* Electrical retest every 12 months or after use	✔
Lamps Dry battery, rechargeable cells	✔
Propane and paraffin	✔
Communication Equipment (see page 184 for particular equipment as to precise frequency of test)	
Cutting Equipment (Oxy-Propane and Oxy-Acetylene)	✔
Radiation Quartz-fibre dosemeter **Equipment**	✔
Dose rate (radiation survey) meter:	✔
0–100 mSv	✔
0–3 mSv/hr or 0–3 Sv/hr	✔
Training	✔
Contamination meter *Note:* Calibration test every 2 years	✔
Plastic Gauntlets	✔
Hydrants	
Air Lifting Units	✔
Axe (Insulated Handle)	✔
Gastight chemical protection suits	✔
Winches and wire ropes	✔
Miscellaneous Gear	✔

Before drills	After operational use or drill	Daily	Weekly	Monthly	3 Monthly	6 Monthly	12 Monthly	Page
					✔		✔	
	✔	✔	✔					
				✔				
		✔	✔					
	✔			✔	✔			
	✔		✔				✔	
	✔							
	✔		✔		✔		✔	
	✔		✔		✔		✔	
	✔		✔		✔			
	✔		✔		✔			
	✔				✔			
						✔	✔	
	✔			✔	✔			
	✔					✔		
	✔			✔	✔			
	✔				✔		✔	
	✔				✔			

1. Pumps (self-propelled and portable)

All pumps should be subjected to the following tests:

(a) On Acceptance and Quarterly Output Test

Pumps should be tested by pumping from open water, using one length of hose per delivery. The length of test should be at least 15 minutes, and any pump found incapable of sustaining the pressure indicated below with a lift as near as possible to, but not exceeding, 3 m from the surface of the water to the pump inlet should be made the subject of a report.

Nominal output of pump at 7 bar l/min	Pump test pressure minimum bar	Number of hose lines	Size of nozzles mm
4500	5.5	2 2	28 25
4050	5.5	4	25
3600	5.5	3	28
3150	5.5	1 2	28 25
2700	5.5	2 1	25 20
2250	5.5	4	20
1800	5.5	3	20
1350	5.5	2	20
900	5.5	2	15
450	5.5	1	15

Notes:

1. Where the nominal output of a pump falls between any two figures in the table, the number and/or size of the nozzle(s) should be adjusted accordingly.

2. Pumps having a capacity below those shown above should be tested to about 75 per cent. of the performance specified by the makers.

(b) On Acceptance and Quarterly Vacuum Test

This test should be carried out immediately after the output test given above.

(1)   All lengths of suction should be coupled up to the suction inlet of the pump with a blank cap in position at the end of the last length but with the blank caps left off all deliveries. The primer should be run at priming speed for not more than 45 seconds. Priming should cease after obtaining 0.8 bar vacuum and the compound gauge needle should then be watched. If the needle falls back to 0.3 bar in less than 1 minute an excessive air leak is present. This may be due to a defective pump gland, to leakage at compound or pressure gauge connections, delivery valves, cooling water connections or to faults in the suction hose or couplings. Any leak should then be rectified, if possible. A pump gland should be adjusted when the pump is running and must not be tightened to the point where water ceases to drip when the pump is working under pressure.

A leak in the suction hose may be found by the water pressure test detailed below, *which should not be carried out as a routine but only when it is necessary to detect a leak.*

(2)   The blank cap on the last length of suction hose should be removed and the suction connected by a suitable adaptor to a hydrant, the static pressure of which does not exceed 3 bar. One delivery should be opened to allow air to escape and the hydrant should then be turned on slowly. The delivery should be shut down as soon as water commences to flow from it and the full pressure of the hydrant allowed to build up. If the hydrant pressure is in excess of 3 bar, one delivery should be left open and the hydrant should then be opened sufficiently to allow the test pressure to build up to the required amount, which should not exceed 3 bar. Any leak present will be indicated by the water flowing from it, and steps should be taken to rectify it.

When carrying out this test:

(i)   the hydrant must not be turned on until the pump delivery valve is open;

(ii)   the pump delivery valve must be closed slowly.

(c) Six Monthly Deep Lift Test

It is desirable that both self propelled and light portable pumps should be subjected to a deep lift test of between 3.5m and 7m at intervals of six months where facilities are readily available.

When a deep lift test is carried out it should be as follows:

Pumps with a capacity greater than 900 1/min at 7 bar	6–7m
Pumps with a capacity between 450 and 900 1/min	5–6m
Pumps with a capacity below 450 1/min	3.5m

Notes:

1. The lift in each case should be measured from the centre of the suction inlet to the surface of the water.

2. The time required for priming should not exceed six seconds per metre of lift.

3. When working on a deep lift the output of the pump will be substantially below its nominal output.

The normal output test indicates the pump performance and the vacuum test checks the efficiency of the primer and exposes any leaks in the suction hose and pump. It is unlikely that a pump which passes both of these tests will fail to pick up water on a deep lift. Therefore, where facilities are not readily available the deep lift test may be omitted.

2. Stirrup Pumps

Stirrup pumps should be examined and got to work on acceptance, quarterly and after operational use. They should be oiled or greased as necessary, checked to see that valves operate correctly and that glands and stuffing boxes do not leak. Faults in a pump should be rectified where this is possible; if not, the pump should be sent in to the workshops for repair.

3. Hose (delivery, suction and hose reel)

(a) Delivery hose

Delivery hose should be tested on acceptance, every 12 months and after operational use. For delivery hose a 12.5 mm nozzle at the branch should be used and for the hose-reel hose the hose reel branch should be used. If a 12.5 mm nozzle is not available then the smallest suitable nozzle which will allow the requisite pressure to be obtained should be employed. If a shut-off branch is used it must not be closed until all air has been expelled.

All delivery hose and hose-reel hose should be tested to a minimum pressure of 10 bar or 1.5 times the normal working pressure where this is higher than 7 bar. Where the pump is incapable of attaining the necessary pressure the maximum pump pressure should be applied.

The pressure should be built up gradually in order to allow sufficient time for the hose to take the strain. Any defects should be suitably marked and the hose sent for repair. All couplings should be examined at the same time for distortion, defective washers should be replaced and the plungers of instantaneous couplings should be lightly oiled or greased and adjusted if necessary to ensure proper seating.

(b) Suction hose

All lengths of suction hose should be examined on acceptance, quarterly and after operational use to see that couplings are in good condition and that washers are in place. Defective washers should be replaced. Collars and threads should be lightly oiled or greased if necessary. The hose should be subjected quarterly to the tests described in Test No. 1(b) 'Pumps — Vacuum Test'.

4. Hose reel equipment

The hose reel equipment on all appliances should be tested on acceptance and quarterly to the appropriate pressure as specified in the test for hose (Test No. 3(a), para. 2) by operating the pump. The correct operation of the branch and tightness of all couplings and glands should be checked and adjustments made if necessary.

5. Nozzles and branches

Nozzles should be examined on acceptance and every six months to ensure that the inside section is truly circular and that no scratches or indentations are present. Any nozzle with a suspected defect should be tested under pressure. Alternatively all nozzles may be tested under pressure.

Diffuser, hand-controlled and adjustable jet branches should be tested under pressure, on acceptance and every six months and should be operated to check that they are working satisfactorily. Branches and nozzles giving an unsatisfactory jet should be sent for repair.

Instantaneous couplings on branches should be examined for distortion.

6. Escapes

The following test and examination procedure should be carried out on acceptance, quarterly, after operational use and on such other occasions as are considered.

(a) Tests

(i) *Strings and rounds*

The escape should be pitched to its full working height hove up in the carriage with the head resting against a building and chocks should be placed in position. A line should be made fast to each string between two adjacent rounds at the centre of the middle extension. The weight of two men should be applied to each line (four men in all) and then released, when the escape should resume its normal position. The line must not be made fast to a round only.

If the officer in charge of the test considers that the escape whips or flexes excessively under the test load, he should request its removal for expert examination and repair if necessary.

After this test a man should ascend the escape and jump the rounds to test the rounds and sockets. (It is not necessary to jump the rounds of a steel escape). The proper method of testing the rounds by jumping is to transfer the weight of both feet simultaneously sharply downwards from each round to the next with feet separated as far as the strings will permit. The height of the jump should not be increased nor should a jump be used to deliver a violent blow to the round. When jumping rounds a man should adopt a comfortable stance, gripping two adjacent rounds firmly at points between the levels of the hip and shoulder. The man should be prepared for a round failure under test. An escape, the rounds of which are to be jumped, should be pitched as nearly vertical as safety considerations permit, the head being secured when necessary to obtain stability, and at least two men being on the levers.

In order to test the top rounds which cannot be jumped, a line is to be made fast by a round turn and two half-hitches at the centre of the top round of the upper extension. The weight of two men is to be applied to the line and then released. this test is to be repeated on the second, third, and such other rounds that cannot be tested by jumping, and also to any special tube or bar fitted for lowering lines to run over.

(ii) *Carriage Wheels*

The hubs of the carriage wheels should be tested for excessive side play by alternately pulling and pushing opposite spokes near the hub. The total side play measured at the hub must not exceed 1.5mm. This test is to be performed when the escape is on an appliance (i.e. when there is no load on the wheels).

(b) Examinations

(i) *Escape*

The escape should be examined, special attention being paid to the following points:

A That moving parts are clean and adequately lubricated;

B That extending and carriage gear cables are correctly rove and run freely through the various pulleys;

C That wire ropes show no sign of excessive kinking or needling (See Test No. 10 Wire ropes);

D That positive pawls and friction brakes on extending and carriage gears are functioning correctly;

E That ladder pawls are operating correctly;

F Hooks, which the extending and carriage wire ropes are secured to, to ensure that the mousing is in good order, or that the steel clips, used in place of mousing on some types, are in position;

G The rounds of wooden escapes at the point where they enter the sockets, and to carriage and lever wheels (if of wooden construction) for signs of rot or other deterioration.

161

H The rubber tread covers on the rounds on metal escape ladders, should be checked for secure fitting.

(ii) *Escape Mounting and Securing Gear*

Before placing the escape on the appliance the mounting and securing gear should be examined for defects, and after the escape has been shipped, the securing gear should be examined for correct fit and functioning. The weight of two men should then be applied to the levers to ensure the escape is secure. Any visual warnings should also be examined for correct operation.

(c) Annual Examination

Every 12 months the following additional examination should be made unless the escape is subjected to an annual examination and test in brigade workshops.

The escape should be lowered and placed horizontally, with the head resting on a trestle. Gears, shafts, bearings, pulleys, pawls and split pins should be examined to see that they fit and function correctly, and that they are sound and free from excessive wear. Nuts, screws, riveted joints and welded joints should be examined for tightness, soundness and freedom from cracks or fractures.

7. Ladders (extension)

These ladders should be examined and tested on acceptance, quarterly, after operational use, and on such other occasions as are considered necessary.

(a) Tests

In the following tests the reference to the jumping of rounds applies only to wooden ladders. It is not necessary to jump the rounds of metal ladders. In order to test the top rounds of ladders which cannot be jumped, a line should be made fast at the centre of the top round of the upper extension by means of a round turn and two half-hitches. The weight of two men should be applied to the line and should then be released. This test should be repeated on the second, third, and such other rounds that cannot be tested by jumping.

(i) *13.5m Extension ladders.*

The ladder should be pitched to its full working height with the head resting agianst the building and the heel of the ladder approximately one quarter of the working height away from the building against which it is pitched. (Where props are fitted they should be replaced in the clips). Two lines should be made fast to the centre of the round at the centre of the middle ladder section and the weight of three men applied as evenly as possible to the lines and then released, when the ladder should resume its normal position.

Extending lines (where fitted) should be tested by applying the weight of two men as described for 9m/10.5m extension ladders (see (ii) below), with the exception of the test in the fully extended position.

(ii) *9m and 10.5m Extension Ladders*
Each ladder should be pitched to its full working height with the head resting against a building. For both 9m and 10.5m, the heel should be approximately one quarter of the working height away from the building against which it is pitched. A line should be made fast to each string between two adjacent rounds at the centre of the overlap of the two sections of the ladder and the weight of three men applied, as evenly as possible to the two lines and then released, when the ladder should resume its normal position. The line must not be made fast to a round only. After this test a man should ascend the ladder and jump the rounds (see illustration on page 161).
The extending line should be tested by applying the weight of two men. The ladder should be pitched without being extended against a wall or building; the weight of two men should then be applied to the line as for extending the ladder as low as practicable, while another two men apply their weight to the extension to prevent it moving. The remaining part of the line should be tested by applying the weight of two men as before but with the ladder fully extended.

Note: It may be convenient for this latter part of the test to be carried out while the ladder is still extended after jumping the rounds.

(iii) *Three Section Short Extension Ladder*
The test for this ladder is the same as for the 10.5m ladder except that the line by which the load is applied should be made fast to the strings, in the prescribed manner, at the centre of the middle ladder section. Being a metal ladder the jumping of the rounds is not necessary, (see 7(a) above) and as the ladder is a push up type there is no line to test.

(iv) *Short Extension Ladders*
The section of short extension ladders should be tested separately. Each section should be pitched at a working angle with the head secured, and as many of the rounds as possible should be jumped (see illustration on page 161). The ladder

should then be reversed and the remaining rounds should be jumped.

(b) Examination (all ladders)

Ladders should be examined for any movement of the timber, for looseness of bolts, rivets or screws in the fittings, for loose wedges and to see that the shoulders of the rounds fit closely up to the strings. Riveted and screwed joints of metal ladders should be examined to ensure that they are tight, and welded joints of metal ladders should be examined to ensure that there are no cracks.

With extension ladders special attention should also be paid to the following points:

(i)   that moving parts are clean and adequately lubricated;

(ii) that extending lines and wire ropes are correctly rove and run freely through the various pulleys;

(iii) that ladder pawls are operating correctly;

(iv) that anchorages for lines and wire ropes are secure;

> *Note:* When extension ladders are placed on the appliance the mountings and securing gear are to be examined to ensure that they fit and function correctly.

(c) Annual Examination (13.5m Extension Ladders only)

Every twelve months the following additional examination should be made unless the ladder is subjected to an annual examination and test in brigade workshops.

The ladder should be placed horizontally on two trestles. Shafts, bearings, pulleys and pawls should then be examined to see that they fit and function correctly and that they are sound and free from excessive wear. Nuts, screws, riveted and welded joints should be examined for tightness, soundness and freedom from cracks or fractures.

8. Turntable ladders

Turntable ladders should be tested and examined by a qualified operator on acceptance, quarterly, after operational use, and on such other occasions as are considered necessary.

Tests should be carried out on reasonably level ground and in calm weather. Where a detachable cage is provided, it should be fitted for these tests.

(a) Tests

(i)   *Load Test*
      A line (or lines) should be attached to the head of the ladder or,

in the case of a ladder with a cage, to the cage.

The ladder should be elevated to 30 degrees in line with the chassis, over the bonnet, then extended to the maximum permissible extension for one-man loading (or one-man in cage as appropriate). The weight of two men should then be gradually applied to the line.

> *Note:* Some late model Magirus ladders with 2-man cages, cut-out at the input for 2-man loading when the cage is fitted. For such ladders the test should be made at that limit and the weight of 3 men applied to lines.

For a ladder with a four-man cage, the ladder should be extended to the maximum permissible extension for two-man loading and the weight of four men applied to the lines attached to the cage.

On completion of the load test, the ladder should return to its unloaded condition and show no signs of stress.

(ii) *Cut-out Tests*

After the load-test, the ladder should be rehoused and extended again at the same elevation (30 degrees) to the normal cut-out point for that particular ladder. If the cut-out fails to operate at this point the ladder should be extended a further one pawl or 'rounds-in-line' position only and, if the cut-out is still not operating, extension should be stopped. The ladder should be elevated to 75 degrees and extended to maximum extension in order to test the maximum extension cut-out.

In the case of a ladder fitted with cage, ladder-head or remote controls, this test should be repeated using those controls, and a further check should be made to ensure that they are inoperative when base control is selected for use.

(iii) *Mechanism Test*

The load and cut-out test procedure will automatically check all ladder operations except training and plumbing. The ladder should, therefore, be trained through 180 degrees and back again and, at the same time, the satisfactory operating of the plumbing gear should be checked.

In the case of a ladder fitted with cage, ladderhead or remote controls, this test should be carried out using all those controls as well as the base controls.

> *Note:* The normal extensions at 30 degrees elevation at which the various types of ladder should cut-out are as follows:

A. *MERRYWEATHER*
Just beyond the extension shown on the one-man scale.

B. *MAGIRUS*
Just beyond the extension shown on the one-man scale when the field-of-operations indicator makes contact. (See also the Note concerning some late model Magirus ladders in section 8(a)(i)).

C. *METZ and PIERREVILLE*
On these ladders the point of cut-out is dependent on ladder loading and, with no load at the head of the ladder, cut-out will occur about three 'rounds-in-line' positions beyond the one-man scale extension. The extension at this cut-out point should be recorded in the appliance logbook or appropriate record for reference.

(b) Examination
The turntable ladder should be examined, special attention being paid to the following:

(i)   That moving parts, including slides and roller tracks, are clean and adequately lubricated;

(ii)   That cables show no excessive kinking or needling (see Test No. 10 'Wire Ropes');

(iii)   That pulleys are running freely;

(iv)   That ladder pawls, where fitted, are operating correctly;

(v)   That the axle-locking mechanism is functioning correctly;

(vi)   That load indicators, where fitted, are operating correctly;

(vii) That communications equipment is functioning correctly;

(viii) That there are no hydraulic fluid leaks from the mechanism or from the jacks;

(ix) That the cage attachments, where applicable, are secure and function correctly.

(c) Technical Inspections
In addition to the quarterly test and examination described above special technical inspections, of the type described in the *Manual of Firemanship*, Book 5, Ladders and Appliances, Chapter 10 'Working with turntable Ladders', should be made at regular intervals, preferably every 6 months. These inspections should only be carried out or be supervised by personnel qualified for this purpose.

9. Hydraulic platforms

Hydraulic platforms should be tested and examined by a qualified operator on acceptance, quarterly, after operational use and on such other occasions as are considered necessary.

(a) Tests

These tests should be carried out on level ground with the jacks lowered. The cage should be loaded with suitable ballast to the maximum permissible load as indicated on the cage.

(i)   *Cut-out tests*

For these tests the base controls should be used, set to override the cage controls where this is not automatic. After the ballast has been loaded the booms should be rehoused on the headrest. The lower boom should then be raised to its maximum elevation and the cut-out for the upper boom tested by raising this boom to its maximum elevation. Where the maximum elevation of the upper boom is limited by the travel of the hydraulic ram, the test for the cut-out must be carried out with the lower boom at an angle specified by the manufacturers. The upper boom should then be lowered to bring the cage to the ground.

(ii) *Mechanism test*

The weight equivalent of one man should then be removed from the platform and an operator should enter the cage. All operations, i.e. the raising and lowering of both booms and rotating in both directions, should then be carried out by the use of the cage controls and also by the use of the base controls to test that they override the cage controls. The cage should then be lowered to the ground and the ballast should be unloaded before the booms are housed on the headrest.

Note: Where the upper boom is fitted with a telescopic or hinged extension arm, the tests should be carried out with the extension arm in its operated position, i.e. in line with the upper boom or fully extended as the case may be.

(iii) *Auxiliary power units*

The auxiliary power unit should be tested by operating all movements in turn.

(b) Annual Test

Every twelve months the following tests should be carried out, or be supervised, by personnel qualified for the purpose.

(i)   The quarterly test but with 25 per cent overload.

(ii) The platform loaded as for the quarterly cut-out test (i.e. the overload should be removed). Both booms should be raised to maximum elevation and the angle measured between the back of the upper boom and the vertical. This angle should be within the limit specified by the manufacturers.

(iii)   The test should be repeated with the lower boom fully depressed and the upper boom raised until the cut-out operates. The back of the upper boom should then be at an elevation as specified by the manufacturers.

(c) Examination

An examination should be made to see that there are no fluid leaks from the mechanism; this should be done both before and after the tests described above. The jacks should be operated to ensure that the feet pivot freely.

Communications equipment should also be checked to ensure that it is operating efficiently.

(d) Technical Inspections

In addition to the quarterly test and examination described above, special technical inspections should be made at regular intervals preferably every 6 months. These inspections should only be carried out or be supervised by personnel qualified for the purpose.

10. Wire ropes

Reference is made in the tests for escapes and turntable ladders to the examination of wire ropes, and the following information is intended for the guidance of those carrying out these examinations.

Wire rope will weaken through normal wear which is usually apparent to the eye when the outside strands of the wire rope assume a smooth and polished appearance. The most important cause of weakening in a wire rope, however, is the fracture of individual wires, generally referred to as needling. This is most likely to occur where a wire rope is subjected to repeated flexing and the part of the wire rope most likely to be affected in this way is that portion which winds round a drum. The general practice in the Fire Service is to replace wire ropes when needling is apparent over much of their length but in any case the number of broken wires should not be allowed to exceed $2\frac{1}{2}$ per cent in any length of ten diameters. This means that for a rope with 37 wires per strand the number is about 6; for a rope with 24 wires per strand the number is about 4, and for one with only 12 wires per strand the number is only 2, in a length of about 150 mm on a 16 mm diameter rope.

After examination, wire ropes should be treated with petroleum jelly.

11. Belts (hook belts, safety belts, rescue slings, harnesses and stretchers)

Hook belts, safety belts, rescue slings, harness and stretchers should be tested and examined on acceptance, quarterly, after operational use and before use for drills.

(a) Tests

Belts should be tested by buckling the belt to its full extent, clipping the hook or 'D' ring on to a suitable anchorage and submitting the belt to the weight of two men suspended from it.

Slings and harness should be tested by securing the lifting ring to a suitable anchorage and submitting each loop of the sling or harness to the weight of two men suspended from it. Stretchers fitted with a lifting ring should be given a similar test.

> *Note:* In order to retain the form of a belt during the load test, it should preferably be buckled round a suitable wooden block, and the load should be applied by means of a bar through the block, or by short lines attached to the block.

(b) Examination

The belts, slings, harness and stretchers should be carefully examined for any signs of wear or deterioration, particularly in the stitching. Hooks and buckles should be checked to see that they function properly and that the tongues are not loose.

12. Lines

The lines specified in (a) below should be tested on acceptance, quarterly, after operational use and, in the case of rescue and lowering lines, before use for drills. In addition all lines should be examined quarterly and after operational use and at such other times as are considered necessary.

(a) Tests

(i) *Rescue and lowering lines, long and short lines*

One end of the line should be secured to an immovable object in such a way that the line and any splices incorporated in it will be subjected to the test. Six men spaced out at intervals of about 1.5 m should take up positions at the free end of the line and when all are in position the front man should apply a steady pull to the line. The remaining men should successively apply a steady pull to the line until the line is being tested by the combined strength of all six men. The combined pull should be maintained for about 20 seconds and then, the men should release the pull in succession from the rear. The line should then be reversed and the test repeated. When lines terminate in an eye splice and snaphook, the snaphook should be attached to the immovable object and when lowering lines have spliced legs, each leg should be tested separately.

An equivalent alternative test is to suspend the line from a suitable anchorage, and to apply the weight of three men. If space does not allow the full length of a line to be tested, the test should to applied to about one half of the line at a time.

(ii) *Guy lines, escape lines and breathing apparatus guide lines*
These should be similarly tested, except that the pull of only two men should be applied or the weight of one man in the case of a suspended line.

(iii) *Mechanical testing*
Where suitable mechanical or hydraulic testing equipment is available these means may also be used. Such tests should subject a line to a steady strain not exceeding that imposed when testing a line by the alternative suspended method, i.e. rescue and lowering lines, long and short lines 225 kg, guy lines, escape lines and breathing apparatus guide lines 76 kg.

(b) Examination (all lines)
The whole length of the line should be examined about 300 mm at a time and should be turned to reveal all sides of that 300 mm before passing on to the next. Hawser-laid ropes should be slightly untwisted locally at intervals of not more than 300 mm to reveal the inner surface of the strands; the strands must be returned to their original position afterwards.

The main causes of deterioration and the signs by which they may be recognised are described in the *Manual of Firemanship*, Book 2 Chapter 10 'Deterioration of rope'. Attention should also be given to the whippings, splices and fittings, such as swivels, snap hooks etc. to ensure that they are free from defects.

13. Safety device (Everest Static Safety Anchor) and anchorages

Safety devices should be tested on acceptance, quarterly, and before use for drills. A check test of the locking mechanism should also be made before each descent. In addition, safety devices should be examined quarterly and on such other occasions as are considered necessary. The mechanism should be dismantled and examined in workshops every six months.

(a) Safety Device

(i) *Test*
The safety device should be attached to an immovable

object, and the line should be rove through the device to within one metre of the free end. One man should pull sharply on the line to lock the mechanism and the line and mechanism should then be subjected to the steady pull of six men as for the test for lines (Test No. 12(a)(i)). During the repeat test with the line reversed the safety device should remain at the free end of the line.

If space does not allow the full length of the line to be tested, it should be tested in sections, the mechanism being locked for each test.

Alternatively the device may be attached to an anchorage (see para. (b), below), and the weight of three men applied to the line, the test being applied to the line in sections according to the height of the anchorage. This method stresses the line to the same degree as a horizontal pull of six men and has the advantage of testing both the anchorage and the safety device simultaneously.

In order to test the eye splice on the end of the line the load must be applied below the eye. This may be done by two men applying their weight to the belt, thus testing the belt, and by the third man applying his weight to the hook connecting the belt to the line, using if necessary a short piece of line for the purpose.

(ii) *Check Test*

Before the line is attached to a man it should be pulled sharply to check the correct operation of the locking mechanism. The mechanism should then be unlocked by a slight pull on the free end of the line.

(iii) *Examination*

The line should be examined in accordance with Test No. 12(b) 'Examination of Lines'.

The safety device should be examined for external damage, particular attention being paid to the pulley flanges.

(iv) *Six Monthly Examination*

Every 6 months safety devices should be dismantled in the workshops and examined in accordance with the manufacturers' instructions.

(b) Anchorages

Fixed anchorages and rounds or other anchorages on turntable ladders and hydraulic platforms to which an Everest device may be attached should be tested by having a line made fast to them and the weight of three men applied. The line should be made fast to the centre of the round or bar.

For this test a turntable ladder should be elevated to not less than 40 degrees and extended to any convenient length within the 2-men-safe scale.

If desired these tests can be applied with the device so that both anchorage and device are tested simultaneously (see third paragraphs (a)(i) above).

14. Breathing apparatus

Each set of breathing apparatus should be examined and tested on acceptance, monthly and after operational use or drill. In addition a General Check of the apparatus should be made by each individual at any time when taking over a set.

(a) General Check

The General Check should be carried out by personnel nominated as Wearers, in the case of:

(i) Whole time stations, immediately after the roll call at the change of Watch and, as necessary, at other times during the Watch.

(ii) Retained stations, at the commencement of a drill period.

(iii) Officers personal sets, at the commencement of a tour of duty.

The General Check should be in accordance with the manufacturers instructions to ensure that the apparatus and ancillary equipment is complete and functioning properly. The mask and carrying harness should be adjusted for the wearers personal use and the provisions of the 'Operational procedure for the use of breathing apparatus' should be complied with. The results of the check should be entered in the appropriate station record.

(b) Monthly Test (and after use)

Each set of breathing apparatus should be examined and tested, in accordance with the manufacturers instruction taking into account any additional central guidance, on acceptance, at least once per month and after operational or training use.

(i) Carrying frames, harness and buckles should be carefully examined for signs of wear; facemasks and goggles should be carefully examined to ensure that they are in good condition. Fittings for ancillary equipment should be checked to ensure that they are satisfactory.

(ii) If the set has been worn it must be thoroughly washed, disinfected, dried and tested: the manufacturers' instructions should be followed as to materials and equipment to be used.

(iii) Before fitting the replacement cylinder on the apparatus the pressure should be checked, using the standard gauge, and noted. After the cylinder is fitted to the apparatus the pressure reading on the set gauge can then be compared with that of the standard gauge, thus checking its accuracy.

(iv) Standard gauges and testing equipment should be checked periodically.

(c) Low cylinder pressure warning whistles

If a low cylinder pressure warning whistle fails to operate between the pressures specified in the tests the apparatus should be placed out of commission until the fault has been rectified.

(d) Cylinders

(i) Periodic Inspection and Test
Cylinders should be kept in circulation and at intervals not exceeding 5 years must be subjected to an inspection and hydraulic stretch test by an approved authority. This does not apply to ultra-lightweight cylinders which must be inspected and tested at 3 yearly intervals. Any cylinder failing the test must be taken out of service.

(ii) Changing of Cylinders
Cylinders showing a pressure reading of less than 80 per cent of their maximum capacity should be replaced by fully charged cylinders. They should be marked MT to avoid confusion.
Cylinders removed from the set and awaiting recharge should not be completely emptied. The valve should be kept completely closed and a blank cap fitted to the outlet.

15. Breathing apparatus ancillary equipment

The following equipment except guide lines and personal lines which are tested quarterly, should be examined and tested, on acceptance, monthly, after operational use or drill and after a battery has been replaced. It is not practicable to have a test for dry batteries. They should therefore be renewed at regular intervals or after a prescribed time of operational use.

(a) Communications equipment

(i) Examination
All items of speech reception and transmission equipment, including face masks, should be examined for defects, damage, or deter-

ioration. Cables should be examined throughout their length for cuts and abrasions. End connections should be examined for defects. Batteries should be examined to ensure that contact points are clean and that no sulphation has occurred.

(ii) Test
Face masks should be connected to the appropriate breathing apparatus set and given a low-pressure test. The equipment should then be donned by two men and tested for clear speech and reception. The test should be repeated with the spare headset, where issued.

(b) Distress signal unit

(i) Examination
The securing strap, fastenings, and the casing should be examined for damage or deterioration. Openings, e.g. horn cones and keyway, should be checked to see that they are free from accumulated dust or dirt and should be cleaned as necessary, taking care that dirt or moisture does not enter the openings. Batteries should be examined to ensure that the contact points are clean and that no sulphation has occurred and should always be removed from units withdrawn from operational use for any reason to avoid the possibility of batteries leaking and causing corrosion inside the unit. MN 1300 batteries are inherently resistant to leakage but the base may 'frost over' with a film of potassium carbonate after some use. This may interfere with the electrical contact and batteries should be examined periodically and any frosting removed with a damp cloth.

(ii) Test
The push button should be pressed and the horn allowed to sound for about 5 seconds. To cancel, the key should be inserted; at the same time the fit of the key should be checked.

(c) Guide and personal lines

(i) Examination
Guide lines and personal lines used with breathing apparatus should be examined in accordance with the procedure set out in Test No. 12 (b). Where personal lines have an outer cover of plastics material this should be examined for cuts and abrasions. Hooks and 'D' rings should be examined to see that they are free from defects, and that the serrations on hooks are clean. Line carriers and pouches should be examined for wear and damage; particular attention should be given to press or other fastenings.

(ii) Test

Guide lines should be tested in accordance with Test No. 12 (a)(ii) and, in the case of combined guideline/communication cable the above mentioned test should be followed by Test No. 15 (a)(i) and (ii).

(d) Lamps

Lamps used with breathing apparatus should be examined in accordance with Test No. 19.

16. Resuscitation apparatus

Each set should be tested in accordance with the manufacturers instructions on acceptance and weekly, after operational use or drill. Cylinders should be checked to see that they contain a full pressure of gas (usually 120 bars). Rubber parts such as masks, valves and bellows used with some types should be examined to ensure that they are not perished and are working freely. After each occasion when a set is worn, the mask and tubing should be disconnected, and thoroughly washed and disinfected.

Cylinders must be subjected to an inspection and test at intervals not exceeding 5 years as described for breathing apparatus cylinders.

17. Extinguishers

(a) General

Where examination, maintenance and testing has been carried out in accordance with paragraphs (b) to (l) below, it is no longer considered necessary for periodic pressure tests to be carried out. If any extinguisher is seen to be showing signs of corrosion or damage either internally or externally during the acceptance, quarterly inspection or examination or after the discharge test, it should be taken out of service.

It may be convenient for the annual discharge test of an extinguisher to take place at the same time as one of the quarterly examinations.

The date of the last discharge of every extinguisher, and the total weight (where applicable), should be recorded on the extinguisher itself or on a suitable tag attached thereto.

It has been recommended that Halon extinguishers in use in the Fire Service should only contain CBM Halon 1011, BCF Halon

1211 or BTM Halon 1301 or in certain circumstances mixtures containing Halon 1011 and 1.1.1. trichloroethane or Halon 1211 and dichlorodifluoromethane.

The tests specified below are applicable only to those in use by the Fire Service. Officers called on to advise occupiers of private or commercial premises in which extinguishers are installed should suggest compliance with the current British Standard Code of Practice. 'BS 5306—1980—Fire extinguishing installations and equipment on premises—Part 3 portable extinguishers.'

(b) Water (soda-acid) type

Chemical extinguishers of the soda-acid type should be opened up for examination on acceptance, quarterly and the following maintenance carried out:

(i) The liquid level should be checked and any slight loss should be made up with water, otherwise a new charge should be used.

(ii) The nozzle, strainer, vent holes in the cap and (where fitted) the internal discharge tube and snifter valve should be checked for cleanliness.

(iii) Before the headcap is replaced, the plunger or other operating device should be checked to see that it operates freely; the washer should be examined and replaced if necessary and the cap should then be tightly screwed to the container to form a gastight joint.

(iv) Hose (if fitted) should be in good condition.

(v) No corrosion or damage should be visible either externally or internally.

Each extinguisher should be tested by discharge once a year, this period to date from the last occasion when the extinguisher was discharged, whether at a fire or for test purposes.

(c) Water (gas-cartridge) type

This type of extinguisher should be opened up for examination on acceptance, quarterly and the following maintenance carried out:

(i) The liquid level should be checked and the liquid topped-up as necessary. The original charge should be retained in the extinguisher.

(ii) The nozzle, strainer, vent holes in the cap and (where fitted) the internal discharge tube and snifter valve should be checked for cleanliness.

(iii) The gas cartridge should be weighed and the weight checked against that marked on the cartridge. The cartridge should be renewed if a loss of more than 10 per cent of the contents is recorded. A check should be made to see that the sealing washer is in good condition.

(iv)   Before the headcap is replaced and while the gas cartridge is unscrewed the plunger, or other operating device, should be checked to see that it operates freely; the washer should be examined and replaced if necessary. The gas cartridge should be replaced and the cap then tightly screwed on to the container to form a gastight joint.

(v)   Hose (if fitted) should be in good condition.

(vi)   No corrosion or damage should be visible either externally or internally.

Each extinguisher should be tested by discharge once a year, this period to date from the last occasion when the extinguisher was discharged, whether at a fire or for test purposes.

(b) Water (stored-pressure) type

This type of extinguisher should be inspected externally on acceptance and quarterly, e.g. nozzle, discharge pipe and for corrosion effects. Also check indicator to ensure extinguisher is pressurised. As it is pressurised it can only be opened for examination after discharge and it should therefore be tested by discharge on acceptance and thereafter once per year.

This period to date from the last occasion when the extinguisher was discharged whether at a fire or for test purposes. The pressure indicating device should be checked before the extinguisher is discharged and after it has been recharged to ensure that the extinguisher is pressurised correctly.

After discharging the extinguisher the following examination should be carried out:

(i)   The nozzle, strainer, vent holes in the cap, and (where fitted) the internal discharge tube should be checked for cleanliness.

(ii)   Discharge hose (where fitted) should be in good condition.

(iii)   Before the headcap is replaced, the plunger or other operating device should be checked to see that it operates freely; the washer should be examined and replaced if necessary and the cap should then be tightly screwed to the container to form a gastight joint.

(iv)   No corrosion or damage should be visible either externally or internally.

(e) Foam (chemical) type

This type of extinguisher should be opened up for examination on acceptance and quarterly, care being taken not to mix the two solutions accidentally otherwise the extinguisher will have to be recharged. The following inspection should be carried out at this time:

(i)   The liquid levels in the body and in the inner container should be checked. Any slight loss may be made up with water, otherwise a new charge should be used. (It is no longer considered necessary to stir the contents of the two containers during examination).

(ii)   The nozzle, vent holes in the cap and snifter valve (where fitted) should be checked for cleanliness.

(iii)   Before the headcap is replaced, the plunger, the headcap lever for the sealing device, or other operating device, should be checked to see that it operates freely. The washer(s) should be examined and replaced if necessary and the cap should then be tightly screwed to the container to form a gastight joint.

(iv)   No corrosion or damage should be visible either externally or internally.

Each foam extinguisher should be tested by discharge once a year, this period to date from the last occasion when the extinguisher was discharged, whether at a fire or for test purposes.

(f) Foam (mechanical) (gas-cartridge) type

This type of extinguisher should be opened up for examination on acceptance and quarterly and the following maintenance carried out:

(i)   The liquid level should be checked. Any slight loss may be made up with water, otherwise a new charge should be used. Where the foam concentrate is in a separate container, this should be checked for leakage.

(ii)   The branchpipe, strainer, vent holes in the cap, the internal discharge tube and the snifter valve should be checked for cleanliness.

(iii)   The gas cartridge should be weighed and the weight checked against that marked on the cartridge. The cartridge should be renewed if a loss of more than 10 per cent of the contents is recorded. A check should be made to see that the sealing washer is in good condition.

(iv)   Before the headcap is replaced and while the gas cartridge is unscrewed, the plunger, or other operating device, should be checked to see that it operates freely, the washer should be examined and replaced if necessary. The gas cartridge should be replaced and the cap then tightly screwed to the container to form a gastight joint.

(v)   Hose should be in good condition.

(vi)   No corrosion or damage should be visible either externally or internally.

Each extinguisher should be tested by discharge once a year, this period to date from the last occasion when the extinguisher was discharged, whether at a fire or for test purposes.

(g) Foam (mechanical) (stored-pressure) type
This type of extinguisher should be externally inspected on acceptance and quarterly, e.g. branchpipe, hose and corrosion effect. As it is pressurised it can only be opened for examination after discharge, and it should therefore also be tested by discharge on acceptance and thereafter once per year, this period to date from the last occasion whether discharged at a fire or for test purposes. The pressure indicating device should be checked before the extinguisher is discharged and after it has been recharged to ensure that the extinguisher is pressurised correctly.

   After discharging the extinguisher the following examination should be carried out:

(i)   The branchpipe, strainer, vent holes in the cap, and (where fitted) the internal discharge tube should be checked for cleanliness.

(ii)   The hose should be in good condition.

(iii) Before the headcap is replaced, the plunger, or other operating device, should be checked to see that it operates freely; the washer should be examined and replaced if necessary. The cap should then be tightly screwed to the container to form a gastight joint.

(iv)   No corrosion or damage should be visible either externally or internally.

(h) Carbon dioxide type
This type of extinguisher should be examined on acceptance and quarterly and the following maintenance carried out:

(i)   The total weight should be checked against that recorded when the extinguisher was put into service. If a loss of weight of more than 10 per cent of the contents is detected the extinguisher should be discharged and returned to the suppliers for examination, test and recharging.

(ii)   The body of the extinguisher should be examined and if there are signs of damage or extensive external corrosion the extinguisher should be discharged and returned to the suppliers for examination, test and recharging.

(iii) The horn, hose and valve assembly should be in good condition. The squeeze-grip horn control (where fitted) should move freely. (This must not be confused with any squeeze-grip actuating mechanism on the valve assembly).

It is not considered advisable that cylinders filled with carbon dioxide for fire-fighting purposes should remain charged indefinitely without examination and test. The first discharge, examination, test and recharge should take place ten years after the initial manufacturing test unless the extinguisher has been discharged at a fire, has showed a loss of pressure or weight or has become excessively corroded externally (see (i) and (ii) above).

If after the first examination and test the cylinder is certified as in a satisfactory condition, it may continue in service for a further period of ten years, subject to the exceptions mentioned above. Thereafter, extinguishers should be discharged, examined, tested by the suppliers and recharged at intervals of five years unless discharged at a fire.

(j) Vaporising liquid (Halon) (stored-pressure) type

This type of extinguisher may contain chlorobromomethane (CBM) Halon 1011, bromochlorodifluoromethane (BCF) Halon 1211, bromotrifluoromethane (BTM) Halon 1301 or, in certain circumstances, mixtures containing Halon 1011 and 1.1.1 trichloroethane or Halon 1211 and dichlorofluoromethane.

These extinguishers are of two types.

(1) those where the operating head and pressurised body are connected and cannot be separated while the extinguisher is charged; and

(2) those where the pressurised body is in the form of a removable and expendable container.

Type 1. The following examination should be carried out on acceptance and quarterly:

(i) Any pressure-indicating device should be checked to see that the correct pressure is being maintained within the extinguisher body.

(ii) The extinguisher should be weighed to detect any loss of the liquid contents. (The weight of the fully charged extinguisher should be recorded at the time of recharging).

(iii) The nozzle should be checked for cleanliness.

(iv) No damage or corrosion should be visible externally.

Each extinguisher should be tested by discharge at intervals not exceeding five years, this period to date from the last occasion when the extinguisher was discharged, whether at a fire or for test purposes.

Note: This type of extinguisher can only be recharged by the suppliers to whom it should be sent after discharge.

Type 2. The following examination should be carried out on acceptance and quarterly:

(i)   The operating head should be unscrewed, the safety catch released, the visual indicator (if fitted) removed, and the operation of the mechanism checked.

(ii)   Any pressure-indicating device should be checked to see that the correct pressure is being mantained within the extinguisher body.

(iii)   The extinguisher should be weighed to detect any loss of the liquid contents. (The weight of the fully charged extinguisher should be recorded at the time of charging.)

(iv)   The nozzle should be checked for cleanliness.

(v)   No damage or corrosion should be visible externally.

Each extinguisher should be tested by discharge at intervals not exceeding 5 years from the date of the last occasion when the extinguisher was discharged, whether at a fire or for test purposes.

(k) Dry powder (gas-cartridge) type

This type of extinguisher should be opened up in a dry atmosphere on acceptance and quarterly and the following examination carried out. Where a discharge control is fitted on the nozzle at the end of the hose this should be operated before opening the extinguisher to ensure that there is no pressure present in the extinguisher.

(i)   The extinguisher should be weighed to check that it contains the correct weight of powder. The weight when fully charged should be recorded at the time of charging.

(ii)   The powder should be agitated to ensure it is free from caking. Protection should be worn from inhalation of powder particles. (See note on page 183).

(iii)   The gas cartridge should be weighed and the weight checked against that marked on the cartridge. The cartridge should be renewed if a loss of more than 10 per cent of the contents is recorded. A check should be made to see that the sealing washer is in good condition.

(iv)   The nozzle and discharge control (if fitted) and the vent holes in the cap should be checked for cleanliness.

(v)   Before the headcap is replaced and while the gas cartridge is unscrewed, the plunger or other operating device should be checked to see that it operates freely, the washer should be examined and replaced if necessary. The gas cartridge should be replaced and the cap then tightly screwed to the container to form a gastight joint.

(vi) Hose (if fitted) should be in good condition.

(vii) No damage or corrosion should be visible either externally or internally.

(viii) Each extinguisher should be tested by discharge every two years—this period to date from the last occasion when the extinguisher was last discharged.

(l) Dry-powder (stored pressure type)

This type of extinguisher may be either 'Factory sealed and refilled' or 'field refillable type' both types are pressurised and can only be opened up for examination after discharge. The following inspection should be carried out on acceptance and quarterly.

(i) The extinguisher should be weighed to check that it contains the correct weight of powder. The weight when fully charged should be recorded at the time of charging.

(ii) The pressure-indicating device should be checked to see that the correct pressure is being maintained within the extinguisher body.

(iii) The nozzle and discharge control (if fitted) should be checked for cleanliness.

(iv) Hose (if fitted) should be in good condition.

(v) No damage or corrosion should be visible externally.

Factory sealed extinguishers should be tested by discharge every 4 years and then returned to the manufacturer for maintenance and refilling.

Field refillable type extinguishers should be tested by discharge every 2 years, this period to date from the last occasion when the extinguisher was last discharged.

At the time of each discharge the opportunity should be taken to examine those parts of the extinguisher not accessible at the quarterly examination, i.e:

(vi) The strainer, vent holes in the cap and (where fitted) the internal discharge tube should be checked for cleanliness.

(vii) Before the headcap is replaced, the plunger or other operating device should be checked to see that it operates freely and the washer should be examined and replaced if necessary. The cap should then be tightly screwed on to the container to form a gastight joint.

(viii) No corrosion or damage should be visible internally.

(ix) Refill in accordance with the manufacturers instructions.

Notes:

1. Dry powder extinguishers must be thoroughly dry internally before they are recharged.

2. Protection in the form of a suitable mask should be worn to minimise the inhalation of powder particles when agitating the powder on inspection, particularly where ingredients are poisonous as with some chlorides employed.

3. Effective means should be provided to ensure that extinguisher bodies are not over pressurised.

18. Gloves (electrical protection)

Gloves carried on appliances should be examined on acceptance, quarterly and after every occasion on which they are used. They should be carefully examined, both inside and out, to detect punctures cuts or scratches, care being taken not to wrench the fingers of the gloves apart nor to subject the gloves to any undue strain. Damaged gloves should be taken out of service. In cases of minor damage gloves may be submitted for re-test.
Gloves should also be submitted for electrical re-test after being used, or in any case at intervals of not more than twelve months in accordance with the current British Standard. After examination, gloves should be coated inside and out with purified talc BP.

19. Lamps

(a) Dry battery type electric hand lamps
These lamps should be checked daily for correct operation; they should also be examined on acceptance and operated weekly and after operational use or drill. The battery should be removed to see that sulphation has not set up between it and the case, contact points should be cleaned if necessary. The battery should then be replaced and the lamp operated to see that it is in working order. It is not practical to have a test for single discharge dry batteries. They should therefore be renewed at regular intervals or after a prescribed time of operational use.

(b) Lamps with rechargeable cells
Sealed rechargeable cells are designed to be maintenance free. Lamps fitted with this type of cell should be checked daily for

correct operation and examined on acceptance, weekly and after operational use. The cells should be recharged periodically and after use.

(c) Propane and paraffin type lamps
These should be examined and tested on acceptance, and monthly in accordance with the makers' instructions.

20. Telecommunications equipment

1. Telephones and teleprinters

Fire Service operational telephone systems should normally be tested in both directions at least once daily. If during abnormal conditions, there is any reason to expect failure of telephone systems (as a result, for example, of unusual weather conditions), additional tests should be made as necessary to ensure that faults do not go undetected.

All switchboard cords should be included in daily tests.

Teleprinters are self-monitoring and do not require periodic tests.

Faults on telephone and teleprinter systems should be reported to the appropriate maintenance authority immediately they are discovered, in accordance with local instructions.

> *Note:* In cases where it is necessary to have regular assistance from telephone exchange operators to facilitate the testing of exchange lines, times for testing should be arranged with the exchange Supervisor.

Exchange lines on automatic exchanges can be tested, without the need for involving exchange operators, by dialling a test call to another exchange line.

2. Fire telephones

Fire telephones (i.e. direct telephone lines between special risks and Fire Service watchrooms or controls) should be tested daily at pre-arranged times agreed with the occupiers of the premises concerned, the brigade to initiate checking action if test calls are not received on time. Test calls are not considered satisfactory unless the name of the building in which the telephone is located is distinctly received by the watchroom attendant and a reply sent back 'Test call (name of building) all correct'.

3. Automatic fire alarm systems

Automatic fire alarm and detector systems installed in factories and other premises which have unmonitored direct line signalling circuits to Fire Service watchrooms or controls should be tested periodically at times agreed with the occupiers of the premises concerned. Checking action should be initiated by the brigade if test calls are not received on time.

4. Turn-out bells, lights, and PA systems

Fire station turn-out bells, lighting systems, and PA systems used for turn-out purposes, should be tested daily by actuation from the central control as well as by actuation of local fire station control switches.

5. Call-out installations

Installations for calling-out retained firemen, should be tested as follows:

(a) Radio pocket alerter systems
It is recommended that firemen's radio pocket alerter systems should be tested weekly from the central control by actuation, of both the 'Test' and 'Fire' signal. The weekly tests should also include a test from the control switches of the local station transmitter(s) of both 'Test' and 'Fire' signals.

(b) Remote Control Systems
Remote control systems which have no fault alarm facilities should be tested daily. Those which have fault alarm facilities should be tested not less than once weekly. The detailed procedure for testing remotely controlled call out installations varies with the different types of system used.

6. Radio equipment

The master-station equipment is self monitoring but a daily test on mobile and hand held equipment is required.

All personal or portable radio equipment should be tested not less than once weekly in accordance with standing instructions, particular care being taken to ensure that batteries are in good condition and adequately charged.

Regular and efficient battery maintenance is absolutely essential to the performance of mobile and portable radio equipment. A comparatively small drop in battery output is sufficient to seriously affect equipment performance, and although this may not always be noticeable when using sets under good conditions or over short distances it will be increasingly evident over longer distances or when working in areas of poor reception.

21. Cutting equipment (oxy-acetylene and oxy-propane)

Cutting equipment should be examined and tested on acceptance, quarterly and after use. The contents of cylinders should also be checked monthly.

(a) Monthly

The contents of the cylinders should be checked by opening the cylinder valves and proceeding as shown in paragraph (viii) or (ix) of the quarterly test.

(b) Quarterly and after use

The test should be carried out as follows:

(i)   Check all threaded connections to ensure that they are tight.

(ii)   Visually inspect hose for signs of damage or deterioration such as cuts, cracks, burns, or wear. Check that hose clips are secure.

(iii)   Open cylinder valves and regulators and set to normal working pressures. Close blowpipe valves and check all connections for leaks using soapy water. Check blowpipe valves in the same way, and apply soapy water to the cutting nozzle to check for leakage past the valves.

(iv)   Dry thoroughly with a clean cloth.

(v)   Check goggles and sparklighter.

(vi)   Light up the blowpipe and visually check for preheat flame.

(vii) Check the operation of the cutting oxygen control and visually check the stream with the blowpipe still alight.

(viii) Shut off the blowpipe, and if regulators are fitted with pressure gauges, check cylinder contents (see Note 1). Close the cylinder valves and open the blowpipe valves to release the pressure in the hoses. Unscrew the pressure regulating screws on the regulators and finally close the blowpipe valves and stow equipment ready for use.

(ix)   After closing the cylinder valves, disconnect preset gaugeless regulators where fitted and connect a test gauge to each of the oxygen and acetylene cylinders to check the contents (See Note 1). Disconnect propane cylinders and weigh the cylinder, the gross weight being compared with the net weight figure stamped on the cylinder to give the propane content. Re-connect the equipment to the cylinders and make ready for use, checking finally that all connections are secure, that all valves are closed, and that any pressure has been released from the hoses.

Notes:

1. *Contents of Cylinders.* Oxygen, acetylene, and propane cylinders should be replaced whenever the contents have fallen to the minimum required to give a satisfactory period of cutting for emergency purposes. The required minimum should be determined in accordance with the type of apparatus, the capacity of the cylinders when full, and the nominal cutting duration of the equipment. The contents of oxygen cylinders may be determined from pressure gauge readings. The contents of dissolved acetylene cylinders may be approximated from pressure gauge readings, or if an accurate determination is required, the cylinder should be weighted, the gross weight being compared with the net weight stamped on the cylinder. Propane cylinders should always be checked by weighing.

The net weight of dissolved acetylene cylinders in grams is stamped adjacent to the cylinder serial number. Propane cylinders have the empty and full weight stamped on the valve boss.

(For calculation purpose dissolved acetylene weighs 1.1 grams per litre, and propane 1.9 grams per litre).

2. *Hose.* Hose may be tested for leakage by immersion in water under working pressure. In the case of worn ends these

may be cut back and refixed. Damaged or suspect hose should be scrapped and replaced.

3. *Regulators*. To avoid possible damage to regulators, they should be unscrewed to the 'no pressure' position before cylinder valves are opened.

If the regulator creeps, e.g. gas is passed when the regulating screw is released, or pressure is built up on the low pressure side when the blowpipe valve is shut, the regulator should be returned to the maker for repair. If gauges do not return to zero when the pressure is released and main valves are closed, the gauges should be returned to the maker for repair or replacement.

4. *Blowpipes*. Leakage from any part of the blowpipe may be detected by one or more of the following means:

(a) A hissing sound;
(b) Smell;
(c) Bubbling on the application of soapy water.

Such leakage may be remedied as follows:

(i)   Leakage around the valve spindle—by tightening the gland nut.
(ii) Leakage at the head nut—by cleaning the head and nozzle and seatings with a soft cloth and retightening the nut.
(iii) In the case of leakage past the valve seatings, and where leakages as in (i) and (ii) cannot be cured—the blowpipe should be returned to the makers for repair.

5. *Cylinders*. Leakage around the valve spindle when the valve is open will be revealed by a hissing sound or by a smell of gas, and may be cured by tightening the gland nut. The test is with soapy water. Leakage when the valve is closed will again be revealed by a hissing sound or by a smell, but in cases of suspected leaks where no indication is present, the valve outlet should be immersed in water, or be tested by the application of soapy water, when leaks will be indicated by bubbles.

If leakage cannot be cured by firmly closing the valve, the cylinder should be moved into the open away from fire and other sources of heat and the suppliers should be advised.

Before any cylinder is connected to apparatus the cylinder valve threaded outlet should be checked to see that the threads are undamaged, the cylinder valve being opened momentarily to blow out dust or other foreign matter which may have entered the outlet.

(It is not advisable to immerse the valve completely when testing the outlet by immersion, as water may find its way into the valve and may give rise to corrosion of the spindle, and consequently, the valve may become difficult to operate).

6. *Precautionary Measures:*

(a) Oils or grease of any kind **must not be used** to lubricate any part of the apparatus.

(b) Where cutting equipment is carried on an appliance it should be stowed away from any oils or grease, oily or greasy rags, etc. This also applies to any reserve cylinders either carried or in store, as contamination of the valve of oxygen cylinders could cause an explosion. Acetylene and propane cylinders should be stowed upright, and the equipment should be so secured that the cylinders cannot fall or make violent contact with one another or come into contact with electrical apparatus or live wires. Hose should not be coiled around the cylinders or regulators. Hose and fittings should be secured in such a manner that they do not suffer damage and that valves cannot be opened accidentally during transit.

(c) Cylinder valves should always be closed when the equipment is not in use.

22. Radiation instruments and equipment

The testing and calibration of radiation instruments should only be carried out by personnel who have received sufficient training to be regarded as a 'competent person'. Whilst this section deals with the testing of instruments and the equipment used for that purpose it does not include the subject of handling radioactive sources which should form part of the training of a 'competent person'. However, it should be noted that **direct contact with** radioactive sources must be avoided.

Radioactive sources of different strengths to source type 'A' will be introduced in the near future. In these circumstances the tests should be modified in accordance with the manufacturers instructions.

Future research and development will undoubtedly result in the emergence of a new generation of instruments, in these circumstances it is therefore important to ensure that any instruments which are not included in this section, are tested and calibrated in accordance with the manufacturers instructions.

Abbreviations:

mSv =	millisievert
Sv =	sievert
mSv/hr =	millisievert per hour
Sv/hr =	sievert per hour

(when working with instruments not calibrated in SI units, 100 millirads = 1mSv).

The exposure, to radiation, of personnel regularly engaged in the testing of radiation instruments should be limited to one millisievert (1mSv) per week, this can only be assured if a dosemeter of a type which will record doses in millisieverts is worn when handling radioactive sources during training and whilst testing instruments.

1. Quartz-fibre dosemeters No. 2A 0–50 millisieverts (0–50 mSv)

Dosemeters should be examined on acceptance, weekly and after use at a fire or other incident, and a calibration test should be carried out every 12 months.

(a) Examination

The dosemeter should be examined to see that the fibre is not markedly out of vertical, and that the fibre and scale calibrations are not blurred or misted. The reading on the dosemeter should then be recorded and, when cumulative weekly readings have reached 10mSv the quartz-fibre should be returned to the zero mark by charging using the charging unit.

If the reading on the dosemeter is more than 7mSv ($3\frac{1}{2}$ minor divisions on the scale) on two successive weekly readings, the instrument should be withdrawn from service.

(b) Calibration Test

The dosemeter should be calibrated annually in accordance with the manufacturers instructions.

2. Quartz-fibre dosemeters No. 7 0–2 millisieverts (0–2 mSv)

(a) Examination

The dosemeter should be given the same weekly examination as the doseimeter No. 2A, and should be recharged to zero as necessary.

The leakage rate should not exceed 2% (0.04 mSv) of the scale in twenty-four hours, i.e., the leakage should not be more than 0.28 mSv (just under three divisions of the scale) between weekly readings.

(b) Calibration Test
The dosemeter should be calibrated annually in accordance with the manufacturers instructions.

3. Doserate (radiation survey) meter 0–100 millisieverts per hour (0–100 mSv/hr)

Survey meters should be examined and tested on acceptance, weekly, after use at a fire or other incident and checked quarterly against a radioactive source. A calibration test should be carried out every 12 months.

(a) Examination
The battery lid and the batteries should be removed and the compartment and battery terminals examined for cleanliness. The batteries should be replaced with the positive terminal (brass cap) downwards and the lid replaced. If the battery cells are found to be corroded, they should be renewed.

(b) Battery Test
The switch should be turned to the BATT position. The batteries are satisfactory if the needle on the dial reaches the green line marked BATT. The switch should be advanced to the ON/LAMP position to check the bulb on the dial, finally returning the switch of the OFF position.

(c) Quarterly Check
After the battery test, the meter should be switched on and placed near enough to a suitable radioactive source to obtain a reading on the dial, indicating that the meter is functioning satisfactorily. The switch should then be returned to the OFF position.

(d) Calibration Test
The survey meter should be placed in the special test jig so that the dial can be read from the front or open side of the jig, and the

switch turned to the ON position. A type 'A' radioactive source on its carrying rod should be inserted down through the hole in the top of the jig, so that the source rests in the small recess in the block on the base. A reading of 1mSv/hr should be recorded on the dial of the meter.

The variation from 1mSv/hr should not exceed two minor divisions of the scale below, or an equivalent distance above, the 1mSv/hr mark. As it is difficult to determine accurately these divisions on the scale, they may be estimated to equal approximately twice the thickness of the needle on either side of the 1 mSv/hr mark. If the variation exceeds these distances the meter should be returned to the manufacturers for examination and recalibration.

> *Note:* The casing of the meter should be kept clean and dry. No maintenance or adjustments other than those included in a., b. or c. above should be attempted.

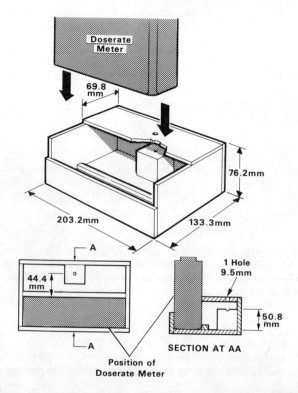

Position of
Doserate Meter

4. Doserate (radiation survey) meter (Wallac RD−8)
0−3 millisieverts per hour (0−3 mSv/hr)
0−3 sieverts per hour (0−3 Sv/hr)

This radiation survey meter should be examined and tested on acceptance, weekly and after use at a fire or other incident and checked quarterly against a radioactive source 'A'. A calibration test should be carried out every 12 months.

(a) Examination

The battery lid and the batteries should be removed and the compartment and battery terminals examined for cleanliness. The batteries and lid should be replaced in accordance with the manufacturer's instructions. If the battery cells are found to be corroded they should be renewed.

(b) Battery Test

The switch should be turned to the TEST position. The batteries are satisfactory if the pointer moves to the green zone of the scale. The switch should then be returned to the OFF position. The scale illumination button should be pressed to check that the bulb is functioning. When the pressure is removed from the button, the light should switch off.

(c) Quarterly Check

After the battery test, the range selector switch should be turned to the mSv/hr position. The instrument should be brought up from a distance and placed near enough to a suitable radioactive source to obtain a reading on the dial indicating that the meter is functioning. The loud speaker should be switched on to check that it is operating.

The range selector switch should then be turned to the Sv/hr scale and the distance of the instrument from the radioactive source adjusted to obtain a reading on the scale. Both switches should be returned to the OFF position.

> *Note:* The mSv/hr scale should always be checked first to avoid damage to the instrument which could occur if the range selector switch is turned from the Sv/hr scale to the mSv/hr scale whilst a radioactive source is in close proximity to the instrument causing more than a full scale deflection of the pointer.

(d) Calibration Test

The survey meter should be placed in the special test jig (see

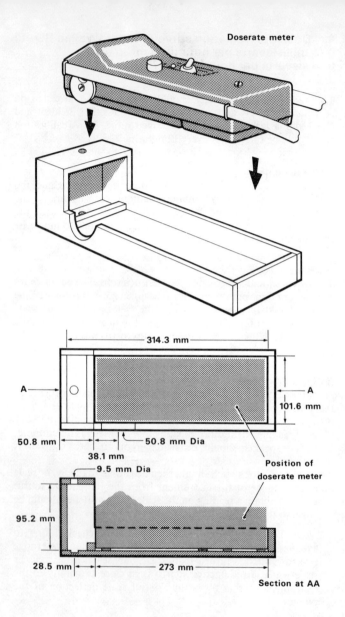

Doserate meter

314.3 mm

A → ← A

101.6 mm

50.8 mm

38.1 mm

50.8 mm Dia

Position of
doserate meter

9.5 mm Dia

95.2 mm

28.5 mm

273 mm

Section at AA

illustration) and the switch turned to the mSv/hr range. A type 'A' radioactive source on its carrying rod should be inserted down through the hole in the top of the jig so that the source rests in the small recess in the base. A reading of approximately 1 mSv/hr should be recorded. The switch should then be turned to the Sv/hr range and a reading of approximately 2 mSv/hr should be recorded. There will be a slight variation between the two readings because there are separate radiation detectors for each scale range and so the distance of the source from each detector is not exactly the same.

The variation from 1 mSv/hr should not exceed two minor divisions of the scale below or approximately one half of a minor division of the scale above. On the Sv/hr scale, the variation from 2 mSv/hr should not exceed approximately one half of a minor division of the scale above or below. If the variation exceeds these tolerances of approximately 20 per cent, the meter should be returned to the United Kingdom agents, for examination and recalibration by the manufacturers.

The casing of the meter should be kept clean and dry. No maintenance or adjustments other than those included in a., b. or c. above should be attempted.

5. Doserate (radiation survey) meter (training)

Training doserate meters should be examined and tested on acceptance, weekly, and checked quarterly against a radioactive source.

(a) Examination

The battery lid and batteries should be removed and the compartment and the battery terminals examined for cleanliness. The batteries and the lid should be replaced in accordance with the manufacturer's instructions. If the battery cells are found to be corroded, they should be renewed.

(b) Battery Test

The switch should be turned to the BATTERY TEST position. The batteries are satisfactory if the needle on the dial reaches the BATTERY TEST position. The switch should then be returned to the OFF position.

(c) Quarterly Check

After the battery test, the meter should be switched on and placed near enough to a suitable radioactive source to obtain a reading on the dial, indicating that the meter is functioning satisfactorily. The switch should then be returned to the OFF position.

6. Contamination Meter

Contamination meters should be examined and tested on acceptance, weekly, after use at a fire or other incident, and checked quarterly against a radioactive source. A calibration test should be carried out every two years, or more frequently if there is doubt about the accuracy of the calibration.

(a) Examination and Battery Test

In the case of battery-operated meters, the lid of the battery compartment and the batteries should be removed and the compartment and the battery terminals checked to see that they are clean. If the cells are found to be corroded they should be renewed, the batteries should then be replaced and tested in accordance with the manufacturer's instructions.

(b) Quarterly Check

Mains-operated meters should be connected to a suitable electricity supply, and both mains and battery-operated meters should be checked against a suitable radioactive source, by operating the switches to all positions, in accordance with the manufacturer's instructions. The switches should then be returned to the OFF position.

(c) Calibration Test

Contamination meters should be returned to the manufacturers to check the calibration at intervals not exceeding two years, or more frequently if there is doubt about the accuracy of calibration.

Note: The casing of the meter and the probe should be kept clean and dry, and when not in use the plastics cover, if provided, should be kept over the face of the probe. No maintenance, or adjustments other than those included in a. and b. above, or as indicated in the manufacturer's instructions should be attempted.

7. Plastic gauntlets

Plastic gauntlets used in connection with radiation work should be examined on acceptance, quarterly and after use.

The gauntlets should be examined to see that they are free from pinholes or splits. Particular attention should be paid to the tips of the fingers and to the palm near the thumb, where damage is most likely to occur.

23. Hydrants

The responsibility for the inspection and maintenance of hydrants rests with the water undertakings, but in many cases agreements have been made with water authorities that inspection and testing may be carried out by the fire authority. It is desirable that hydrants should be inspected twice a year, but they must be inspected and tested at least once a year.

(a) Inspection

Attention should be given to pits, frames, covers and the surface-paving round the edges of the frames, and to the proper marking of hydrants so that they can be found in all conditions of weather or light; indicator plates should be cleaned at each inspection. A hydrant should not be reported in good working order unless all details in connection with it are complete and in order.

(b) Test

Each hydrant should be tested in the following manner, using a standpipe for the purpose.

(i) *Outlet to be tested.* A standpipe should be fitted to the outlet to ensure that the thread or connection is in good order.

(ii) *Hydrant charged.* With a standpipe connected to the outlet, the valve should be partially opened to release a small quantity of water through the hydrant. The flow of water must be directed into the gutter, using a short length of hose, if necessary.

(iii) *Valves to be tested.* With the standpipe still in position a blank cap should be inserted in the head (or the valve in the standpipe head should be closed), and the hydrant opened to its fullest extent. Whilst thus under pressure, all joints should be examined for signs of leakage. The hydrant should then be turned off and, if the blank cap is not fitted with an air release, the standpipe should be unshipped without the blank cap being removed (or the valve in the standpipe head being opened).

(iv) *Frost Valve*. The frost valve (where fitted) should be checked to see that it is in a satisfactory working order.

These tests should not be carried out during frosty weather.

(c) Hydrant Pits

After each inspection or test, and when hydrants have been used at fires, hydrant pits should be left empty and clean.

(d) Special Flow Tests

Where doubt exists as to the capacity of a main and it is necessary or desirable to carry out initial or periodic flow tests, the appropriate water authority should be consulted inter alia in order that arrangements may be made for the attendance, if necessary, of the authority's officials. Discretion should also be used as to the time at which these tests should be carried out.

It will normally only be necessary to carry out flow tests on smaller diameter mains, i.e. 150 mm or below, and where the main is of some length. Advice should be sought from the appropriate water authority as to the situation of mains with a poor supply, unless this information is already available. Such mains should be borne in mind when dealing with fires in the locality.

24. Air Lifting Units

To be inspected and tested in accordance with the manufacturers instructions.

25. Axe, Fireman's with Insulated Handle

Firemen's axes with insulated handles should be examined on acceptance, every six months and on each occasion after use, to detect cuts, scratches or other damage to the handle which might adversely affect its insulating properties. In the event of such damage being discovered, the axe should be taken out of service and sent through the usual channels for an insulation re-test in accordance with the current British Standard.

26. Gastight Chemical Protection Suits

Each gastight chemical protection suit should be:

(a) Examined at monthly intervals; and

(b) Tested:-

(i) On acceptance from the manufacturer's.

(ii) On issue for use when this is not within a period of three months from the date of acceptance from the manufacturer's.

(iii) After each use.

(iv) Following any repair; and

(v) Within three months of the date of the last test, unless a more frequent test is recommended by the manufacturers.

(c) Cleansing and decontamination

Immediately following operational use and before removal from the wearer, the suit should be cleansed and decontaminated in accordance with standard procedure. Following its removal from the wearer, the suit should be thoroughly cleansed inside and out, in accordance with the manufacturer's instructions, and the inside disinfected, particularly around the area of the head and also the boots. When cleansing the suit, it is important that all traces of chemicals are removed in order to avoid damage. Care must be taken to remove any chemicals/dirt located between the teeth of the zip. Following any cleansing operation, the zip should if necessary be lightly lubricated as indicated by the manufacturer's instructions.

Suits once cleansed and disinfected and before being stowed or stored, should be thoroughly dried in accordance with the manufacturer's instructions.

Any suit used at an incident should be carefully examined for signs of mechanical or chemical damage. Subject to any technical advice on the chemicals involved such an examination may need to be repeated after a period of 24 hours has elapsed.

(d) Testing of suits

To ensure that the suit provides the level of protection required for operational purposes the following test procedures should be used.

(i) The suit, including gloves and boots, should be laid out on a suitable flat and clean surface, e.g. table, workbench or smooth floor away from any sources of heat and/or draught.

(ii) Any creases or folds found in the suit should be removed as far as practical and the valves carefully blanked off with appropriate components as recommended by the manufacturer.

(iii)   The suit should be *carefully* inflated to a pressure not exceeding *180 mm* of water, and then allowed to settle for a period of at least *10 minutes* in order to allow any creased areas to unfold, the suit to stretch, the temperature to settle and the pressure throughout the suit to reach equilibrium.

(iv)   Following the period of 10 minutes settling time, pressure in the suit should be *adjusted to 170 mm* of water.

(v)   A further period of *6 minutes* should be allowed to elapse, and during this period, in order to satisfy the requirements of the test, the pressure in the suit should not fall below *150 mm* of water. If the pressure level does fall below 150 mm of water a further detailed check of the suit, mask and test fittings will be required to determine the source of the pressure leak, if necessary using a soap and water solution.

Note: Careful attention must be paid to the cleanliness and the refitting/renewal of valves which have been obstructed or removed in order to carry out the test, to ensure that they function satisfactorily after the test.

27.   Winches and wire ropes

(a) Examination and test
Winches and ropes should be tested and examined on acceptance, on return from a repairer, quarterly and after operational use.

(i)   *Winches.* Check for wear and damage, check operation of winch and lubricate if necessary using recommended oils.

(ii)   *Wire rope.* Check shackle (if fitted) to ensure that there are no signs of strain or distortion and that the shackle pin is in good condition and can be easily screwed in by hand. Examine the thimble and splice for signs of bulging or looseness. Examine the rope along its entire length for signs of wear, kinking or needling (see Test No. 10 Wire ropes page 168).

(b) Annual Examination
Every 12 months winches and ropes should be subjected to technical inspection. These inspections should be carried out, or be supervised by, persons qualified for the purpose.

28.   Miscellaneous Gear

In addition to the other items of equipment for which standard tests are laid down, there are many items of gear carried on appliances which, though no specific test is provided, should nevertheless be examined on acceptance, quarterly and after use to ensure that any moving parts are in good order and that the general efficiency of the equipment has not been impaired either by misuse, lack or attention of other cause. Hydraulic equipment should be examined, operated, and reservoirs topped up as necessary. Any tools which require a sharp edge for their successful operation, should be sharpened as necessary. Items of equipment, such as standpipe heads, foam branchpipes, inductors, etc. which incorporate a strainer or filter should be dismantled in order that the strainer can be cleaned. The mantles on LPG lights should be examined and the contents of cylinders checked by weighing. Hurricane lamps, heater lamps and any other types of oil lamp should be examined, the containers replenished and the wicks trimmed to ensure that they are available at all times for immediate use. Protective clothing should be examined for defects. Salvage sheets should be examined to ensure that they are dry and serviceable.

Squad drill and saluting

Squad drill

General remarks and words of command

Squad drill must be considered from two aspects, firstly as a valuable training exercise and secondly as a means whereby groups of men may be moved about quickly and in an orderly manner.

When members of the Service form up on parade for any purpose they will fall in in three ranks, unless the numbers are insufficient. Five men will fall in in single rank, six to eight men in two ranks, nine or more men in three ranks. If desired, a marker or markers may first be fallen in by means of the command *'Marker(s) Fall-in'*. The drill instructor should teach by illustration as much as possible, either performing the movements himself or causing them to be performed by a man placed facing the squad.

Men should not be kept in the position of 'Attention' for long periods. When explanations are being given to them, men should be given the order *'Stand at Ease'*. If it is intended to rest the men and permit them to move their limbs, but without quitting their ground, the order *'Stand Easy'* should be given. Relaxation of dress should be permitted during training in hot weather.

Every command must be loud and pronounced distinctly, so that it may be heard by all concerned. Slovenly and indistinct words of command result in slackness and hesitation.

Any command consisting of one word must be preceded by a cautionary word; and the cautionary part of a command must be given slowly and distinctly; the final or executive part, which, in general, should consist only of one word or syllable, must be given sharply and quickly as in the following examples: *'Squad—Halt'*; *Quick—March'*. A pause of one second should be made between the cautionary word and the executive word.

Men should frequently be practised in giving words of command, and care must be taken to acquire the correct timing.

In the elementary stages of training Open Order should be adopted for all movements so that the instructor may observe each member of the squad.

The following directions should be adhered to by instructors taking squad drill:

Stand to attention when giving orders. Position yourself so that you can see and be seen, hear and be heard.

Make your orders clear and crisp. Preserve an even and distinct pause between the last syllable of the cautionary and the executive parts of the command.

You must limit words of command to those shown in bold type. No additions are permitted with the exception that when changing direction the preliminary cautions *'Into line'* or *'Into file'* may be used i.e. *'Into line right (or left) turn'* or *'Into file right (or left) turn'*.

Carry yourself smartly when you move about the drill ground. A slack instructor means a slack squad.

If you move with your squad keep in step with it.

Do not chase your squad if you allow it to get too far away. Raise your voice and give the appropriate order.

When calling the roll stand the squad to *'Attention'* while the men answer to their names.

Squad drill

1. Position of attention

'Squad—'Tion'. (Pronounce *'Squad—shun'*). Heels together and in line; feet turned out, at an angle of about 45 degrees; knees straight; body erect; head up, shoulders level and square to the front, down and moderately back; arms hanging easily from the shoulders. Palms of the hands turned towards the thighs, hands partially closed, backs of the fingers lightly touching the thigh, thumb close to the forefinger; eyes looking straight to the front. Breathing should not in any way be restricted (Plates 1 and 2).

2. Standing at ease

'Stand at—Ease'. Keeping the legs straight, the left foot is carried about 300 mm to the left, so that the weight of the body is rested equally on both feet. At the same time the hands are carried behind the back; the back of the right hand is placed in the palm of the left, the fingers and thumb being allowed to grasp it lightly and the arms being allowed to hang easily to their full extent (Plate 3).

3. Standing easy

'**Stand—Easy**'. Men are permitted to move their limbs but without quitting their ground, so that on coming to 'Attention', there is no loss of dressing.

> *Note:* The command 'Stand—Easy' is only given to men standing at 'Ease'. Men 'Standing Easy' who receive a caution such as 'Squad'—will assume the position of 'Stand at Ease'.

4. Formation of a squad

The marker or right-hand man is first placed by means of the command '*Marker(s) Fall—in*'. On the order '*Fall—in*' the remainder fall in one after the other on the left of the marker in three ranks in the 'At Ease' position, dressing by the right, with a distance of 750 mm between ranks; intervals between files is obtained by dressing with intervals.

A file consists of three members of the squad, one in the front rank covered by two in the rear ranks.

A blank or incomplete file will always be the second file from the left. If there are only two in the file, the centre rank will be left blank; if one man only, he will take up a position in the front rank.

5. Dressing

If it is necessary to correct the dressing, the command '*Right (or Left)—Dress*' will be given.

'**Right (or Left)—Dress**'. Each man, except the men on the named flank looks towards the flank by which the dressing has to be taken, the front rank extend the right (or left) arm, hand clenched, and, commencing with the man nearest the named flank by which the dressing is to be made, each man moves up or back to this place successively until he can just see the lower part of the face of the second man from him, each front rank man touches the shoulder of the man on his right (or left) with his knuckles, the two rear ranks covering the front rank.

Each man in succession from the directing flank looks to his front as soon as he has his dressing, the men in the front rank at the same time cut their arms to the side.

Close Order Dress. Where space is limited the order '*Close Order'—Dress to the Right (or Left)*' is given. The drill is as in 'Right (or Left)—Dress' above except the right or left arm is not used but a shoulder to shoulder dressing is taken.

Each man in succession, from the directing flank, looks to his front as soon as he has his dressing.

6. Numbering

'**Squad—Number**'. The right hand man of the front rank calls *'one'*, the next *'two'* and so on in succession to the left, the numbers being called out sharply and distinctly.

Members in the middle and rear ranks will note and adopt the number of the file in the front rank.

7. Sizing a squad

'**Tallest on the flanks, shortest in the centre, in three ranks—Size**'. The squad turn right, break off and arrange themselves, according to their height, in the same rank, the tallest on their nearest flank, and take up their dressing by the right, at the position of 'Attention'.

Note: The instructor will then number the squad and will correct any irregularities in sizing by order numbers to exchange positions as necessary. When all necessary exchanges have been made, the instructor will again number the squad in order to identify individuals in their final positions.

8. Dismissing

'**Dis—miss**'. The squad turn to the right, and after a brief pause, break off quietly.

Note: Members of a parade which is dismissed by an officer will not salute.

9. Length of pace and time

	Length of pace	Time
Quick Time	750 mm	120 paces a minute
Stepping Out	825 mm	120 paces a minute
Stepping Short	525 mm	120 paces a minute
Side Step	300mm	120 paces a minute

10. Stepping forward and backward

'—Paces Forward (or Step Back)—March'. Each man steps forward (or backward) the number of paces ordered, commencing with the left foot. Length of pace to be 750 mm.

Note: This movement is restricted to not more four paces forward or backward.

11. Opening and closing a squad

'Open Order—March'. The front rank take two paces forward and the rear rank two paces backwards.
As soon as the paces are completed, the squad will dress by the right.

'Close Order—March'. The action of the front and rear ranks is reversed and the squad will then dress by the right.

Notes:

1. The order *'Open Order—March'* may be given to men in two ranks when the front rank will step forward two paces.

2. During drill in 'Open Order', markers and blank files will not alter their positions unless the ranks are changed.

3. Men moving forward or backward will keep the arms close to the side.

12. Side step

'Right (or Left) Close—March' or '—Paces Right (or Left) Close—March'. Each man carries his right (or left) foot 300 mm direct to the right (or left) and closes his left (or right) foot to it, thus completing the pace; he takes the next and, if necessary, subsequent paces in the same manner.

Note: Men should not usually be moved to a flank by means of the side step for more than 12 paces.

13. Turning by numbers

'Turning to the Right—One'. Keeping both knees straight, the body erect and the arms steady at their sides, the men turn to the right on the right heel and left toe, raising the left heel and right toe in doing so.

'Two'. The left heel is brought smartly up to the right without stamping the foot on the ground.

'Turning to the Left—One'. The men turn as to the right but on the left heel and right toe.

'Two'. The right heel is brought smartly up to the left without stamping the foot on the ground.

'About turn—One'. The men turn fully about to the right to face in the opposite direction as described for turning to the right.

'Two'. The left heel is brought smartly up tot he right without stamping the foot on the ground.

14. Marking Time

'Mark—Time'. The order *'Mark Time'* is given as the left foot passes the right. The left foot completes its pace, after which the time is continued, without advancing by raising each foot alternately about 150 mm, the knees being raised to the front and arms steady at the sides. At the halt, the word of command is *'Quick Mark—Time'*.

'For—ward'. The order *'Forward'* is given as the left foot is coming to the ground. A check pace with the right foot is completed and men move off again with the left foot at the previous pace and time.

15. The Halt (Marking Time)

(A squad 'Marking Time' and required to 'Halt').

'Squad—Halt'. The command *'Halt'* is given as the left foot is being raised, and the 'Halt' is completed in two mark-time paces.

16. Words of command on the march

The following tables show when to give words of command to men on the move:

'Right—Turn'	The *Cautionary Order* is given as the right foot passes the left.
'Squad—Halt'	The Order is given the next time the right foot passes the left.

'About—Turn'	The *Cautionary Order* is given as the left foot passes the right.
'Left—Turn'	The *Order* is given net time the left foot passes the right.
'Mark—Time'	
'For—ward'	The *Cautionary Order* is given as the left foot is coming to the ground.
	The *Order* is given the next time the left foot is coming to the ground.

Note: The interval between the *Cautionary Order* and the *Order* given above is based on quick time. The instructor should bear in mind the distance between him and his squad, when giving words of command, so that the order is received by the squad on the correct foot.

17. Marching in squad

Before a squad is ordered to march, the directing flank must be indicated by the caution, *'By the Right (or Left)'*. Each man preserves his position in the general alignment by an occasional glance towards the directing flank.

The directing flank when in file is the original front rank and will not be altered.

The directing flank when in line will normally be the original right flank.

18. Marching in quick time

'Quick—March'. The squad step off together with a full pace of 750 mm, with the left foot, in quick time. The arms, which should be as straight as their natural bend will allow, should swing naturally from the shoulders, hands reaching as high as the waist line at front and rear. The hands should be kept closed but not clenched, thumbs always to the front pressing downwards with the thumb will tend to keep the elbows from bending.

19. The Halt (on the move)

'Squad—Halt'. The command *'Halt'* is given as the right foot passes the left. The left foot completes its pace, and the right foot is brought smartly in line with it without stamping.

20. Turning on the march

'Right (or Left)—Turn'. Each man turns on the left (or right) foot without checking the pace.

'About—Turn'. Each man turns about on his own ground in three paces. The fourth pace will be a full pace of 750 mm to march away in the new direction.

Note: When turning on the march, the arms will be kept to the sides at the point of the turn. The proper execution of turning on the march depends entirely on the way in which the word of command is given, e.g. in turning to the right the caution *'Right'* is given as the right foot passes the left, and the executive order *'Turn'* when the right foot passes the left next time. The next pace (left foot) will be in the original direction for the purpose of checking the forward movement of the body. The body is now turned and a full pace taken with the right foot in the new direction.

In 'Turning About', the cautionary and executive orders are given on two successive beats as the left foot passes the right. The next pace will be a full pace to the old front with the right foot, the turn being made during the next three paces, the fourth paces being a full pace with the right foot in the new direction. Whilst the turn is being made the man will remain on the same ground, the knees being raised in 'Marking Time' and the arms kept by the side.

In the case of a squad with a single blank file, marching in line, the blank file will make a check pace and two mark time paces on the word *'About'*, thus gaining his position in the new front rank before the turn is completed.

During drill in 'Open Order', guides and blank files will not alter their positions unless the ranks are changed.

21. Changing direction by Wheeling

(a) In file

'Right (or Left)—Wheel'. The inner man of the leading file moves round a quarter of the circumference of a circle having a radius of 1 m, stepping short to enable the two outer men of the file to wheel with him. When the quarter circle is completed the file will lead on in the new direction. The other files in succession will follow in the footsteps of the leading file.

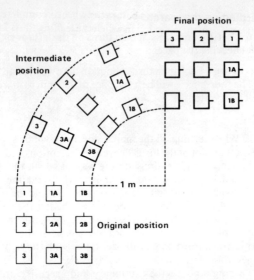

'Rear Files—Cover'. If the squad is halted or ordered to mark time before the whole squad has wheeled into the new direction, the files which have not yet wheeled will cover off on those which have, moving to their places by the shortest route.

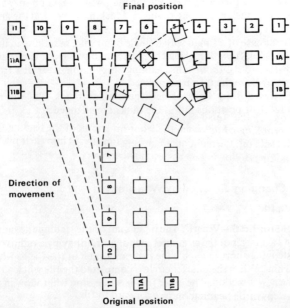

210

If the order 'For—ward' is given before the wheel is completed, the squad will lead on in the direction in which the leading file is facing.

(b) In line

A squad in line may change direction by wheeling, when the action of each rank will be as laid down in (a) above.

22. Changing step on the March

'Change—Step'. The advancing foot completes its pace, and the ball of the rear foot is brought up to the heel of the advanced one, which takes another step forward, so that the time is not lost, two successive steps being taken with the same foot. The arms are kept to the sides during the three change-step paces. This movement must be executed with precision to avoid the appearance of skipping.

Note: The advancing foot is the opposite foot to that on which the executive order is given.

23. Forming Single File from File

'Advance in Single File, Quick—March'. The front-rank man of the leading file marches off, followed by his two rear-rank men who are followed by the front-rank man of the second file, and so on.

Note: If the squad is marching in file, the command will be *'Form Single File'* when the front-rank man of the leading file will lead on, the remainder marking time to get into their places and then following on as described above.

24. Forming File from Single File

'Form—Threes'. The leading man marks time, the remainder of the squad regain their positions in file, marking time as they reach their places.

'For—ward'. The squad moves forward in file.

Notes:

1. If it is desired to halt on the completion of the movement, the command will be *'At the Halt, Form—Threes'*, when the leading man will halt, the remainder halting as they reach their original places in file.

2. When the squad contains between 6 and 8 men, who were originally fallen in two ranks, the order for forming file from single file will be *'Form—Twos'*.

Saluting

1. In the Fire Service it is the custom to salute senior officers when in uniform and for this purpose the naval type salute has been adopted.

(a) Saluting with the hand

The right hand is raised smartly, but naturally to the front of the headgear, the palm of the hand being to the left but inclined slightly inwards, so that the eyes on glancing up can see the inside of the palm, the thumb and fingers being close together, elbow in line with the shoulder, hand and forearm in line, fingers touching the rim of the cap or helmet or front of headgear over the right eye (Plate 4). The salute should be completed by smartly dropping the right hand to the side.

(b) Saluting otherwise than with the hand

When not wearing a cap or helmet or when carrying anything which prevents saluting with the right hand, the member will, if standing still, stand to attention and face the officer as he passes. If walking, turn the head smartly towards the officer on passing.
When passing an officer, the salute should be commenced just before meeting and continued until past.

2. Officers of Station Officer or Fire Control Officer rank and above should receive this salute.

3. Members of the Service when on duty (unless driving a vehicle) should salute in the following circumstances:

(i)   When reporting to or addressing an officer of higher rank who is entitled to a salute.

(ii)   On being addressed or spoken to by an officer of higher rank who is entitled to a salute.

(iii)   On meeting for the first time in the day the officer in charge of the station, provided he is an officer entitled to a salute.

4. When a squad is passing an officer who is entitled to a salute only the member in charge of the squad will salute, at the same time giving the order *'Eyes right'* or *'Eyes left'* to the squad.

5. When officers of different rank are walking together and are saluted, only the senior officer present will acknowledge the salute.

6. All members of the Fire Service should salute during the playing of the National Anthem, unless they are on parade, when the party should be called to attention and the officer in charge of the parade should salute. They should also salute on other occasions where it is generally customary for a salute to be given in a disciplined service. They are not required to salute officers of other services.

7. Officers should, on all occasions, return a salute smartly.

Fitness training

1. Fitness training on stations

1. General

Firemen are from time to time called upon to undertake extremely arduous tasks, which occasionally demand exertion close to their limits of physical strength and endurance. By the nature of the job these physical demands vary in intensity and frequency to such an extent that in many cases they do not occur often enough to maintain a fireman at the peak of physical fitness. The sudden overstretching of a muscle or limb can, at best, produce stiffness lasting several days, or, at worst, an injury which may have permanent effect. It is therefore in the personal interest of all operational members of the service to maintain themselves at a reasonable peak of physical fitness. Safety from injury not only depends upon fitness, but on agility, mental alertness, and speed of reaction.

The exercises set out below are designed for use on stations. They require no special equipment or dress and are such as can be controlled by a junior officer who has no special training as a Fitness Training Instructor. In view of this junior officers are advised against exceeding the exercises outlined unless they are trained as Fitness Training Instructors and are conversant with the full effects of the exercise on each individual concerned. These exercises are designed to take into consideration the wide variation in age of members of any typical watch or group and the fact that often only small numbers of men are available at any one time.

Frequency is relatively more important than length of time. Consequently, a few minutes fitness training several times each week is very much more beneficial than an hour of such training once a month. Where possible a short period of fitness training should precede the more formalised drill activity, thus ensuring that each member of the drill squad is 'limbered up' in preparation for the heavier physical demands.

2. Lifting

In order to understand fully the concept upon which correct lifting techniques are based, it is necessary to learn a little about the construction of the spine. The spine is a hollow column made up of a series of separate interlocking bones known as vertebrae. Vertebrae are separated from each other by a small cushion of resilient tissue. This not only provides a cushion against the shock of landing heavily on one's foot or buttocks but also allows each vertebrae—at least in younger people—to move slightly independently of its neighbour. In certain forward and backward movements the cushions will have a tendency to act as a hinge between the vertebrae. If, therefore, too much strain is applied with the body bent in the forward (or backward) position the hinge can be damaged and may result in a very painful injury. Some of these injuries are referred to as a 'slipped disc'.

To ensure that you avoid such injuries it is necessary that you practice the safe lifting techniques until they become 'second nature'.

Correct lifting technique

When lifting heavy objects the correct practice is to place the load near to the feet, bending the knees and maintaining the spine in a straight posture. When the load is to be raised, the straightening of the legs and maintaining of a straight back places the strain on the powerful leg muscles and not on the back muscles and the lifting therefore requires less effort.

the 'WRONG' method of lifting showing the position of the spine when attempting to lift a heavy weight and indicates the area of possible damage and injury.

Illustrates the 'RIGHT' method of lifting.

Two men lifting technique

When lifting a heavy or sizeable load requiring two men, both men should lift together with the knees bent, back straight and facing squarely on to the load.

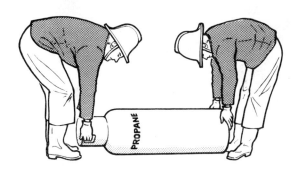

Illustrates the 'WRONG' method with legs straight and backs bent.

The 'RIGHT' method with knees bent, straight backs and facing the load squarely.

It is important when two men are lifting a heavy load together that the load is equally balanced between both men. The ideal is for both men to be of similar height and physique to avoid undue strain on the smaller man.

The 'WRONG' method showing the excess strain on the smaller man.

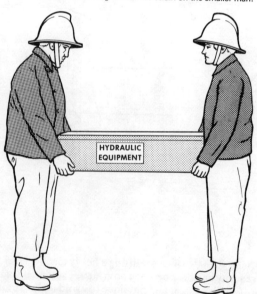

The 'RIGHT' method showing the load equally balanced.

218

When lifting a load down from a height.

It is important to seek assistance when lifting a load from a height or needing to move a load into position for lifting or lowering. Single handed attempts to move a load by jerking gives rise to the danger of causing a serious strain and additionally the possibility of the load falling and causing a more serious injury.

The 'WRONG' method showing the danger of damage to the spine by sudden jerking movements.

The 'RIGHT' method showing the gradual application of load with assistance.

When needing to push a load

The full weight of the body should be placed squarely behind a load whenever it is necessary to push it along. The hands should be placed firmly on the load, so that the weight of the body will be transmitted via the arms to the load to be moved.

Good vision when carrying a load

Never carry a load blindly. Always be able to see where you are walking and any obstructions ahead.

The 'WRONG' method of carrying a load and being unable to see the hazards ahead.

The 'RIGHT' method allowing the carrier to see any obstructions.

Multi-person carrying

When a number of people are carrying a load together it is important that they work as a team and no undue strain is placed on any one individual. Ensure that sufficient men are available to lift and carry the load. The order 'lift' or 'raise', as appropriate, should be given to ensure a concerted effort by timing.

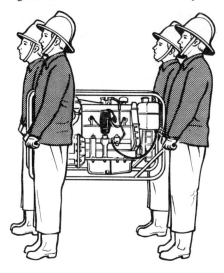

Illustrates the principle of sufficient people to share a load and ease the burden.

Illustrates the use of multi-person lifting by the application of forces at differing points to move or raise a heavy object.

3. Log exercises

Log exercises (using a long pipe or pole—weight approximately 54kg. For 6 men).

(1) Astride, log on one shoulder: Knee bending and stretching with arm stretching upward, alternatively lowering the log to the opposite shoulder.

(2) Astride, log under one arm: Trunk bending sideways towards the log with the opposite arm swinging sideways, upwards and over head, alternating from the left to the right side.

(3) Astride, holding log between legs: Quick passing forward or backward.

(4) Astride, arms upward, holding log overhead: Quick passing forward or backward.

(5) Lying on the back, knees bent, log in crook of arms and resting on the chest: trunk raising with leg stretching.

4. Speed and agility

(a) Sprinting, relay races and fast games of all types.

The following are given as a guide:

   Sprint relay
   Medley relay
   Clock relay
   Wheel relay
   Running out and making up hose
   Rugby pass relay
   Rugby touch
   Netball
   Volley ball
   Ground handball
   Ring the stick

(b) Jumping and vaulting
   Running astride vault (leapfrog)

5. Medicine balls

Paired movements with a medicine ball or bag of sand (weight 3–4 kg) for general strengthening—abdomen, shoulders, girdle, arms and upper spine.

(1) With feet astride, ball held on chest, facing each other. The ball is thrown with both hands from one to the other.

(2) With foot forward, facing each other, ball held behind the head. The ball is thrown as for soccer 'throw in'.

(3) With feet astride standing back to back, one yard apart. The ball is passed alternately backward between the legs and overhead to partner.

(4) With feet astride, facing each other. Relaxed trunk bending and stretching forward, throwing the ball forward to partner.

(5) With feet astride, facing in the same direction. Relaxed trunk bending downward followed by trunk stretching upward, throwing the ball backward overhead to partner.

(6) With feet astride, back to back. Trunk and head turning, throwing the ball sideways and backward to partner.

(7) With feet astride, facing in the same direction. The ball is thrown with both hands backward between the legs to partner.

(8) Overarm bowling position with the ball in one hand. The ball is hurled overarm for height and distance, both to the left and right. The rear foot must not step over the line in front of other foot.

2. Fitness training to be taken under guidance of trained instructor

Physical training tables

1. General

A physical training table is a plan of work, or a table of movements selected and arranged to certain rules for each training period. The training tables are divided into three parts: Part I is the 'limbering up' period, designed to prepare a man to perform without strain the harder exercises which follow; Part II contains the more vigorous exercises for the progressive development of strength, agility, stamina and confidence; Part III is the cooling down and corrective portion of the table.

The time allotted to the whole physical training period determines the proportion of time which can be devoted to Part II, as Parts I and III are always the same, requiring about five minutes and two to three minutes, respectively. In a 30-minutes period, therefore, there will be about 20 minutes in which to concentrate on the more robust part of the table.

Suitable exercises for Parts I, II and III are set out in 'Table planning', and trained instructors should prepare tables to incorporate a variety of the activities listed in order to avoid constant repetition of a few exercises.

Table planning

Set out are three methods of physical training, each based on training periods of about 30 minutes:

Method A deals with exercises suitable for formal classes of, say, six or more men.

Method B deals with small group activities, which may be incorporated with, or used as an alternative to, the Part II activities set out in Method A. It deals in particular with activities where the number of men available is less than six.

Method C deals with *Circuit Training*, which may be used with classes of any size where time and facilities allow the keeping of individual records. This method may also be used alternately with Method A or B.

METHOD A

Training Table: Part I Limbering up

This Part, which should last about five minutes, consists of limbering up activities which should precede the selected exercises forming Part II.

1. Running activities

Medium-paced running interspersed with one or two informal activities, such as 'Reversing Team Direction', 'Chase Him,' 'Touch Four Objects and Back,' 'Running and Jumping High to Touch,' etc. This part of limbering up should not be too vigorous nor last too long.

2. Exercises

A selection of two or three of the following six exercises should then be performed. The trained instructor should not be in too much of a hurry to change from one exercise to another. It is better to perform two exercises properly rather than six badly.

224

(a) Arm and shoulder (Astride, one hand on hip). Arm circling backward vigorously, single or double arm movement.

(b) Trunk (Astride, hands on hips). Trunk circling, with a full range of movement.

(c) Leg (Astride). Jumping with arm swinging (1–4), and with arm swinging sideways and upwards to clap the hands above the head (5–8).

(d) Arm and shoulder (Astride, cross bend, fist clenched). Elbow circling, forward and backward, with shoulder rolling.

(e) Abdomen, arm and shoulder (Front support). Arm bending (1–4), astride jumping (5–8), foot placing forward, left and right (9–12).

(f) Leg Skip jumping, landing in the knee-forward-bend position, with or without turning after every fourth count.

Note: The figures shown in brackets () indicate the number of times a particular movement may be carried out before the next movement is commenced, e.g. (1–4) means that the movement may be carried out once, twice, three or four times according to requirements.

Training Table: Part II General exercises

The selection of activities from the following two groups should be made to last about 20 minutes. The principles of the *'technique of lifting'* set out in 'Fitness training on stations', paragraph 2 should be clearly understood; they can then be applied as appropriate during general training drills with appliances and equipment.

1. Endurance

Running and marching, to be made progressive both in pace and in the distance covered and comprising a mixture of walking, trotting and short sprints, including several exercises en route based on the following:

> Marching on the toes to a given number of steps, i.e. alternatively marching ten steps and running ten steps;
>
> Marching with simple arm movements, i.e. arm bending and stretching upwards, forwards and sideways;
>
> Running with knees raising and with 'about turn' on a given number of steps;
>
> Surmounting various types of obstacle with and without a burden.

2. Strengthening

(a) Pulling and pushing

Pulling on a rope; hauling on a heavy object such as a tree or derrick; tug-of-war; three-, four- or five-cornered tug, using short ropes attached to a central iron ring.

> Team pulling and pushing, using a log (or pipe line).
>
> Rugby scrum.
>
> Pressing forward (by teams).

(b) Abdominal and heaving

Any of the 'stick' exercises shown in *'Small group activities'* on page 228. Hanging with overgrasp: arm bending (using the lower struts of some hose drying towers or horizontally-supported first floor ladders).

Hanging with undergrasp: circling upward and downward using the same type of improvised apparatus.

Training Table: Part III Cooling down activities

The activities should always end the physical training period (two to three minutes).

(a) Marching, with special attention to poise and carriage.

(b) Normal breathing.

(c) Correct position of attention before dismissal.

METHOD B

Small group activities and game-form exercises

These activities, as their name implies, provide suitable exercises where insufficient men are available for ordinary class work. Many of them require no apparatus, but a certain amount of easily improvised equipment will add considerably to the range of possible activities and will increase the purposeful element of the work. Some details of the improvisations recommended are given on page 238.

The 'limbering up' sequence of Part I of Method A should be undertaken for the preliminary warming up, but the usual medium-paced run and informal activities may have to be confined to such movements as 'Running on the Spot', 'Knee Raising', 'Jumping High to Touch', 'Skipping', etc. Part III should follow the normal pattern.

Many of the exercises in Part II of Method A are also suitable for inclusion in small group work, particularly those requiring pairs content work, which produce the best results and also maintain the interest of the men. There is distinct pleasure in the rhythm of a good class working well under experienced control, but when such class work is denied them, men can still find incentive for good and happy physical effort in individual contest.

While it is important, therefore, that suitable exercises from the work listed in Part II, Method A should be included where possible, an additional careful selection from the following game-form and paired exercises should be made to compile Part II for small group tables.

In order to assist instructors to compile a well-balanced series of activities, the following activities also include a guide to the main muscle groups involved.

Without apparatus (paired movements)

(a) Arms and shoulders
'Pushing Contest': With his palms against his opponent's palms, one man tries to push the other over a marked line, or into a base.

(b) Arms and legs
'Pulling Contest': A marked line on the ground divides the partners and one man tries to pull his partner completely over to his side of the line.

(c) Arms and legs
'Pushing Contest': With his hands on his partner's shoulders, one man tries to push his partner over a marked line or into a base.

(d) Arms
'Pushing Contest': Keeping the arms straight, the exercise is performed by pushing first with one arm and then with the other.

(e) Trunk
'Sawing Wood': Grasping each other's hands, paired partners sit on the floor with legs crossed and pull, the body being twisted from side to side as alternate hands are pulled.

(f) Trunk and arms

Standing back to back and grasping each other's wrists, each man swings his arms upwards and downwards from the side position to above the head. The knees should be kept straight, the feet flat on the floor and the body upright.

(g) Trunk and neck

'*Obstinate Mule*': The 'mule' is the man in the kneeling position. The standing partner tries to pull the 'mule' into a marked square, while the 'mule' resists and tries to move backwards. The 'mule' must keep his head bent backwards. A smooth floor is essential.

(h) Trunk and neck

'*Log raising*': One man remains stiff while he is raised by his partner from the back-lying position to the standing position. 'Log lowering' may also be performed.

(j) Trunk and abdomen

One partner sits on the floor keeping his body straight and his legs and trunk at right angles. His partner kneels at his feet and, grasping the ankles, raises and lowers the legs of his partner. The man sitting must keep a right-angle position between trunk and legs.

(k) Abdominal and lateral

Each man lies on his back and grasps his partner's hands. Each man raises his legs to a vertical position, then lowers them sideways until they rest on the floor. This is repeated alternately from left to right. The hands and shoulders must be kept on the floor and the knees must be kept straight all the time.

With apparatus

1. Ropes

Heaving activities for general strengthening, but particularly for the abdomen.

'Three- or four-cornered tug.'

'Jump and Heave.' Jumping up so as to touch the chin to a pre-determined mark on a vertical rope.

Vertical climbing to a mark using the arms and legs, and later, using only the arms.

Various competitive heaves and swings on a 'trapeze' (see e. Improvisation of equipment).

2. Sticks

Paired movements using sticks:

(a) Arms and legs

'Pushing Contest'. A strong stick is held by both partners and, with arms straight, each man tries to push his opponent over the marked line. The stick should be held with the palms downwards.

(b) Arms and shoulders
'*Stick Twisting*'. The stick is held as in (a) above, and each man tries to prevent his opponent from twisting the stick either to the right or left.

(c) Arms and shoulders

'*Forcing Stick Upwards or Downwards*'.

(i)   The stick is held at chest height (undergrip) and one man tries to force it upwards in front of the face.

(ii) The stick is held at the back of the head (overgrip) and one man tries to force it upwards behind his head.

(iii) The stick is held in the upward stretch position (overgrip) and one man tries to pull it downward in front of the face.

(iv) From the same position (overgrip) one man tries to pull the stick downard behind the head.

(d) Legs
'*See-saw*'. With toes touching and grasping a stick in the upward stretch position (overgrip) the partners alternately bend and stretch their knees.

METHOD C

1. Circuit training

One of the quickest and most effective methods of acquiring a basic standard of physical fitness is through *Circuit Training,* a method which is particularly suitable for use in the Fire Service. It requires a minimum of equipment, no special skill, yet demands the maximum effort from each performer and makes a man work against his own past performance so that he is able to see positive proof of his personal progress.

Circuit training has three main characteristics:

(a) It aims at the development of muscular and circulo-respiratory fitness;

(b) It applies the principle of progressive loading;

(c) It enables large numbers of performers to train at the same time, irrespective of varying standards of fitness, by employing a circuit of consecutively numbered exercises around which each performer progresses; each does a prescribed allocation of work at each exercise and checks his progress against the clock.

Ideally, a man should train to his own individual standard at least once a week, although obviously two or three sessions would bring added fitness in a much shorter time. As with other methods of physical training, the session should commence with a short 'limbering up' period (Part I) to get the body warm and the blood flow increased before strenuous effort is undertaken. This enables work to be carried out more efficiently and also lessens the danger of injury. It is equally important that each session should close with a short 'cooling down' period (Part III) and so allow the blood flow and heart action to return to normal. The circuit of exercises is therefore Part II of the training session.

2. The circuit

The following typical circuit is devised to strengthen the muscles of the leg, stomach, arms and back, and to produce a good level of basic fitness; a full circuit should take between 20 and 30 minutes to complete:

(a) Exercise (Leg and general)

'Step-ups': Each man steps on and off a bench, approximately half a metre high. The rhythm should be a 4-count as follows: (1) left foot up; (2) right foot up; (3) left foot down; (4) right foot down. Legs should be straight and the body upright when standing on the bench.

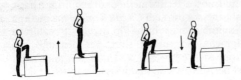

(b) Exercise (Abdomen, legs and general)

'Squat thrusts': Each man maintains a continuous 4-count rhythm, as follows: From a standing position (1) down to the crouch position with flat hands support; (2) the legs jumped back to front support position; (3) the legs returned to the crouch position; (4) straighten up to the start position.

(c) Exercise (Abdomen)

'Trunk Curls': Each man lies on his back with his hands resting on his thighs and raises his trunk, allowing his hands to slide along his thighs as far as the knee-cap; on touching the knees he returns to the back-lying position. The exercise is repeated continuously and rhythmically.

(d) Exercise (Shoulders, back and chest)

'Press-ups': With arms bent in the front support position, each man presses up and down. The body should be kept rigid during the movement.

(e) Exercise (Legs and general)

'Squat Jumps': From the squat position with one foot in front of the other, each man jumps up to stretch the legs and returns to the squat position with the other leg in front.

(f) Exercise (Upper body)

'Chinning': From the overgrasp position hanging on a bar, each man bends his arms until his chin touches the bar, then straightens his arms. This is repeated continuously and rhythmically.

(g) Exercise (Back and general)

'Chest Raising': From a lying-face-down position and clasping his hands behind his back with arms straight, each man lifts his head and shoulders off the floor and pushes his hands towards his feet.

After completing three circuits, the exercise is concluded with:

(h) A Shuttle Run: Each man sprints ten yards flat out, turns and sprints ten yards back. This is repeated five times each way.

3. How to use the circuit

(a) Each exercise should be performed correctly. It is important that the *full range of movements* is gone through each time.

235

(b) Each exercise should be performed as quickly as possible for 30 seconds (or until unable to do more), and the number of repetitions noted. One minute's rest should be taken between each exercise. This is the TEST RATE.

(c) The TRAINING RATE is calculated by halving the test rate.

(d) The TRAINING RATE for each exercise is entered on the progress card (see page 237).

(e) For the first three training sessions the circuite is repeated twice, each exercise being performed at the training rate, with the man *moving immediately* to the next exercise on completion of the previous one.

(f) At the end of the second circuit the shuttle run is performed.

(g) Each man should time himself for the complete session, i.e. from the start of the first circuit to the end of the shuttle run, and should record this time. This establishes a target time, which the man should aim to beat at the next training session.

(h) After three sessions of completing two circuits, an increase should be made to three circuits, and these should be performed in subsequent sessions. The performer should again time himself and record this time as before.

(j) After about eight weeks the margin by which a man will be able to reduce his time for each sessions will be very small. He should now test himself again and from the results he should calculate a new training rate. He will thus get positive proof of increased fitness.

(k) Tests and subsequent alterations to individual training rates should be carried out at intervals of two months.

3. Obstacle course training

From time to time interesting sessions can be composed of work over obstacle courses. In this way variety can be maintained and the competitive spirit introduced. Individual and team times can profitably be taken and will increase enthusiasm amongst the competitors.

Work of this nature must, in itself, be progressive, but it should not be undertaken until men have reached the stage when they are ready to assimilate without excessive strain more strenuous work. Generally speaking, this type of advanced physical training should be designed to develop courage, determination, strength, stamina and control.

PROGRESS CARD (Front)

Exercise	Date	Name:	
		Rates	
		Test	Training
1.	. . . .	. . . .	
2.	. . . .	. . . .	
3.	. . . .	. . . .	
4.	. . . .	. . . .	
5.	. . . .	. . . .	
6.	. . . .	. . . .	
7.	. . . .	. . . .	

PROGRESS CARD (Back)

Training Sessions

Date	Time taken	Date	Time taken	Date	Time taken

The progressive states of training should be:

(i) To teach the quickest and easiest methods of surmounting the various obstacles, one by one, paying particular attention to the conservation of energy through the application of the correct technique;

(ii) To combine two or three obstacles of different types;

(iii) To introduce the competitive element over a few chosen obstacles;

(iv) To practise over the complete course, paying more importance to style and method than to speed;

(v) To increase gradually the number of obstacles for competitive work until the whole range is included.

4. Improvisation of equipment

With the exception of a rope which cannot be improvised, all essential apparatus for physical training for firemen can be devised with very little expenditure of time or energy. A keen instructor will spot the possibilities of the ordinary, everyday things at hand and will find means of using them to advantage. There may be suitable girders from which ropes might be slung. If a bench is not available for bench exercises, a good substitute can be improvised with a plank supported at its ends on petrol tins, small oil drums, wooden blocks or house bricks. A section of short extension ladders when properly supported can be used for heaving and hand walking exercises when it is in the horizontal or oblique position. Some hose-drying towers are so constructed that the lower horizontal struts can be used for heaving, circling up, or other exercises. Climbing ropes should not be less than 38 mm diameter and preferably 50 mm. Thinner rope than this is painful for the hands and difficult to get a leg hold. A rope 4.5 m high is sufficient for normal vertical climbing exercises.

Radio facilities

1. Call signs

(a) All fire service radio schemes are allocated official call signs by the Home Office Directorate of Telecommunications and consist of the prefix 'M2' followed by two or three letters *(Example: 'M2FH')*. Call sign suffixes for outstations are allocated locally by individual fire brigades, and, for mobiles, usually consist of two or three digits *(Example: 'M2FH234')*. For fixed outstations a suffix letter is added *(Example: 'M2FHA')*.

(b) Because call signs are frequently used when tracing interference, it is necessary for official scheme call signs to be frequently used, and the general rule is that it is always used in full by main control operators when they sign off by giving the general clearance at the end of each period of transmission.

(c) It is permissible, and normal practice, to omit the 'M2' prefix during periods of transmission and for outstation users to identify themselves by simply using the suffix digits or letters *(Example: 'FH from 234. Over')*. Any mobile operating on a brigade channel, other than its own, should, however, always use its full scheme call sign *(e.g. M2FH201)* when making preliminary contact with a neighbouring brigade control so as to ensure correct identification. For the same reason the control concerned should acknowledge by quoting its own and the calling mobile's call signs in full *(Example: 'Go ahead M2FH201. M2GH Over')*.

(d) Except in the case of personal sets, the call sign identifies the unit or station—not a particular radio set, nor an individual. Hence, several sets on different channels working in the same station or control room normally carry the same call sign: the call sign of the station or control room.

(e) When pack or personal sets are used, the call signs allocated are usually the rank and surname of the individual to whom the set is allocated. When necessary, identification of the incident at which the set is being used should be added so that fireground messages from two incidents in close proximity can be easily identified.

2. Operating procedures

(a) In any radio scheme there must be one station responsible for the general conduct or signalling and this is normally the responsibility of main control operators. No station may transmit a message without first obtaining permission from the control by means of the standard 'Preliminary Call'. (See paragraph 3(b)(i)).

(b) No outstation should call unless it is known that the controlling station is free to receive. In single-frequency schemes this will be evident if the last transmission ended with the 'General Clearance' or that no other station can be heard transmitting at the time. In double-frequency schemes an 'engaged signal' (a series of 'pips') is radiated while the main control is receiving a signal and calls should not normally be made during such periods. Priority calls from outstations should, preferably be made while the main control is transmitting (see paragraph 3(f)).

(c) Although the calling and answering phrases used by different brigades vary slightly, there are a number of points of good practice applicable to all radio scheme users which, if consistently adopted, greatly improve operating efficiency and maximise channel utilisation, especially during busy periods. The use of standard calling and answering phrases, and call signs, are essential to enable users on a scheme speedily to establish initial contact and for traffic on the channel to be efficiently controlled, but once initial contact has been established it is unnecessary, and in fact undesirable, for these standard phrases to be unnecessarily repeated. It is only when signals are poor and hard to read that it is necessary to repeat procedural phrases and call signs to ensure correct identification.

(d) All mobile and other outstation radio equipment in Fire Service radio schemes operates in the 'simplex' mode (it is not possible to transmit and receive simultaneously as with a telephone conversation); therefore the word 'Over' is used to indicate to the receiving station that the caller is about to switch from 'transmit' to 'receive'.

(e) Most main controls of Fire Service radio schemes, operate in the 'duplex' mode (operators can hear incoming message while an outgoing transmission is in progress). Whilst this does not affect the need for strict usage of the 'Over' procedure, it enables outstation operators to call-in for priority attention while the control is transmitting.

(f) The control operator on any radio channel is responsible at all times for maintaining radio discipline and, by being firm, clear and concise, can do a great deal, especially during busy periods, to speed up radio traffic and achieve maximum use of air time. Outstation users must at all times accept the discipline imposed by main control operators and never proceed with transmission of a message without first making a preliminary call to main control for permission to proceed.

(g) Main control operators must always conclude each period of transmission by broadcasting what is known as the 'General Clearance' which should include the full official call sign of the scheme. The general clearance indicates that previous users have finished for the time being and that the channel is now free for other callers who may be waiting to use it. The operative word in the general clearance is the word 'Out' transmitted in place of the word 'Over' *(Example: 'M2FH-Out')*.

(h) When a number of portable or personal sets are being used (e.g. on a fireground personal set channel) it is essential for one of the users to be nominated as the operator in charge of the channel if confusion is to be avoided. The procedure used by this operator to control traffic on the channel should be the same as that used by main scheme control operators. (See also paragraph 1(e)).

(j) Congestion on radio channels is often aggravated by unnecessary repetition of call signs and procedural phrases as well as by failure to use standard messages and abbreviations. If the simple points of good practice referred to in this section are observed, and the standard message procedure adhered to, general efficiency is greatly improved and radio channel congestion minimised especially during busy periods.

3. Methods of signalling

(a) Both 'direct' and 'broadcast' methods of signalling are used in the Fire Service and examples which illustrate the principles of these two signalling methods are given in the following paragraphs.

(b) Direct method
(for use when two stations are communicating with each other).

    (i) **Preliminary Call.** Which should normally precede a conversation with, or transmission of a message to another radio station:

> *'FH, from 234. Over'.*(Mobile calling Control)
> *'234 from FH. Over'.*(Control calling Mobile)

    (ii) **Response.** The station called replies (without any prefix) with 'Go ahead' (or 'Wait', as appropriate) followed by its own abbreviated call sign and the word 'Over', thus:

> *'Go ahead. FH Over'.*(Control answering Mobile)
> *'Go ahead. 234 Over'.*(Mobile answering Control)

When two outstations call-in simultaneously then Control operator must, in its response, indicate which station is to proceed by quoting its call sign, thus;

> *'Go ahead 234. FH Over'.*

If it is necessary to send a message via another station to one which is outside direct range of the originating station, the latter must make this clear to the intermediate station and quote the call sign of the station to which the message is to be sent, thus:

> '...Pass message to 253. Begins. From...to...etc.'

(c) Broadcast Method

(Usually used by the Control for transmitting the same message to all or a number of outstations). The preliminary calling phrase is transmitted twice, followed by the message (at dictation speed if to be written down) and then repeated at normal speed as a check, followed by 'message ends', thus:

> *'FH calling all stations. FH calling all stations. Begins...ends'.*
> (transmitted twice).

When the attention of some only of the stations on the channel is required, their individual call signs must be clearly quoted, thus:

> *'FH calling 234, 237, 342 and 344* (transmitted twice)... etc.'

Stations called with a broadcast message should acknowledge only when called upon to do so by the calling station, which should bring them in one at a time, thus:

> '...Ends. Origin 14.15. Acknowledge. 234. Over'.
> 'Received. 234 Over'.   (234 acknowledging)
> '237. Over'.   (Control to 237)
> 'Received. 237 Over'.   (237 acknowledging)

...etc., until all have acknowledged after which Control should conclude with the general clearance, thus:

> *'M2FH. Out.'*

(d) Transmission of text of messages

All messages sent by radio must be as brief as possible, and those to be written down by recipients must be transmitted at slow dictation speed. Where appropriate, the phrasing of messages should conform to the Standard message procedures section of this Drill Book.

Unless call signs in themselves are sufficient identification of the addressee and addressor, this must be made clear in the prefix to the message, thus:

> *'FH calling 274. From Chief Officer to Div. Officer Brown. Begins...'*

(e) Outstation to outstation calling

When it is necessary for outstations to speak to each other direct (e.g. mobile to mobile), permission to do so must first be obtained from the main control, thus:

'FH from 234. Talk-through with 317. Over.'

The Control operator replies: *'Go ahead 234. Over'*, leaving 234 to call 317 direct. When finished, the initiating officer (234) should conclude with the word 'Out', when the main control should give the clearance: *'M2FH Out.'*

(f) Priority of attention
Priority of attention should only be requested for **extremely urgent messages;** the method of obtaining it being by use of the word 'Priority' in the preliminary call, thus:

'FH from 234, Priority, over'.

If all radio transmissions are kept as short as possible, there should rarely be any need for a priority caller to break into another station's transmission, but when this is necessary it should preferably be done when the main control operator is transmitting.

(g) Reporting on and off radio watch
In order that the availability of stations 'on the air' may be kept up to date by the control, outstation operators should always report 'On Watch' when they first switch on their sets. Before switching off, operators should report that the station is 'Closing Down'. This type of very brief message may be included in the preliminary call, thus:

'FH from 234. On Watch/Closing. Over.'

(h) Repetitions, corrections and checks
When a transmission is not understood, the recipient should reply with the word 'Repeat', signifying that the transmission should be repeated in full. When parts only of transmissions are involved, the following phrases should be used:

> *'Repeat'/Correction/Check word after/before...*
> *'Repeat'/Correction/Check all after/before...*
> *'Repeat'/Correction/Check all between...and...*
> *'Repeat'/Correction/Check address to/from...*

In the case of very short messages it is usually simpler and quicker to request repetition of the whole message rather than a particular part of it.

In the case of a long message the transmitting station should occasionally pause to check that the message is being received.

(j) Signal strength reports
When reporting the quality of signals received, it should not normally be necessary to use phrases other than the following:

'Loud and clear'

'Weak but Readable'

'Unreadable'

When reporting noise or interference, operators should use their own plain language description which, in the case of interference from another radio station, should include any general information (especially call signs or names) which might assist in tracing its origin.

(k) Phonetic Alphabet

The NATO phonetic alphabet and other aids towards clearness of speech should be thoroughly memorised and used as necessary by all operators and users of radio. It is not normally necessary to use the phonetic alphabet when quoting radio call signs commonly used in ones own radio scheme.

(l) Definitions

The following standard terms are used to save time and should be used consistently by all radio users.

'Over'	Used at the end of any transmission if an answer is required or expected.
'Out'	Used at the end of a transmission when no answer is required or expected. When used by the main control in the 'General Clearance' the word 'Out' signifies that the channel is open for further traffic.
'Received'	Used to acknowledge receipt of a transmission and signifies that the transmission or message has been received, is understood, and will be complied with.
'Repeat'	Used when the recipient has not understood some or all of the message.
'Verify'	Used when requesting verification of the accuracy of information (such as the address of an incident).
'I Spell''	Used immediately prior to spelling out a word, abbreviation, letter or series of letters.

4. General hints for all radio users

(a) Remember that transmissions on fire brigade radio networks are not secure against unauthorised monitoring by members of the
244

public and others. **Therefore messages of a confidential nature should not be transmitted by radio.**

(b) Because radio messages may be overheard by members of the public and others, all messages and other transmissions should be confined strictly to the operational business in hand.

(c) Adhere strictly to authorised radio operating procedure and standard messages and accept without question requests and instructions given by the operator in charge of the channel.

(d) When drafting messages be brief and adhere to standard message phraseology and content. Decide what is to be said before commencing to transmit—hesitation confuses and wastes time.

(e) Make sure you know which channel you are supposed to be working on and check that your set is in fact switched to the correct one. Never switch to another channel without first informing the appropriate control.

(f) Messages should be read clearly and distinctly at such a speed that they may be easily read and if necessary written down. When broadcasting to a number of stations, the second reading may be at a slightly higher speed.

(g) Important or unusual words should be spelt out using the NATO phonetic alphabet, and particular care should be taken when transmitting numerals (see Aids to clearness of speech).

(h) Whenever you are called, indicate immediately that you have heard, even if you must give the instruction 'Wait'. If a message addressed to you calls for a reply which may take time to prepare, **answer** at once, **reply** later.

(j) Speak close to the microphone, keeping the voice at an even level. Do not operate the transmit switch until the microphone is close to the mouth, nor turn your head away whilst transmitting. Do not shout or gabble. Keep your voice pitched normally, emphasise your consonants, and avoid letting your voice drop at the end of sentences or phrases.

(k) When transmitting messages speak in convenient fairly short phrases with a slight pause between each phrase.

(l) After using a hand-microphone, replace it carefully in its holder and ensure that the transmit switch is not left depressed in storage. If a mobile transmitter is left permanently 'On' confusion is caused firstly because that mobile cannot receive calls and secondly it may either block or cause serious interference on the radio channel.

(m) Always observe the 'Engaged' signal (pip tones) unless your message is urgent, in which case use the 'Priority' Procedure (see paragraph 3(f)).

(n) If you suspect for any reason that your equipment is not working correctly, report the facts to control as soon as possible.

(o) The loss of any item of fire brigade radio equipment should be reported to the Police without delay, quoting serial numbers wherever possible.

Aids towards clearness of speech on telephone and radio

(a) When sending names or words:

The vowel sounds should be given their ordinary value and the sound of consonants emphasised.

The phonetic equivalents given below should be used by Fire Service personnel when passing messages by telephone and radio whenever it is necessary to emphasise the identity of letters and numerals.

When using the phonetic alphabet, particular attention should be given to the phonetic pronunciations, emphasis being laid upon the syllables which are underlined.

Letter	*Phonetic equivalent*	*Pronunciation*
A	ALFA	*AL* FAH
B	BRAVO	*BRAH-VOH*
C	CHARLIE	*CHAR* LEE
D	DELTA	*DELL* TAH
E	ECHO	*ECK* OH
F	FOXTROT	*FOKS* TROT
G	GOLF	GOLF
H	HOTEL	HOH *TELL*
I	INDIA	*IN* DEE AH
J	JULIET	*JEW* LEE *ETT*
K	KILO	*KEY* LOH
L	LIMA	*LEE* MAH
M	MIKE	MIKE
N	NOVEMBER	NO *VEM* BER
O	OSCAR	*OSS* CAH
P	PAPA	PAP *PAH*
Q	QUEBEC	*KEY* BECK
R	ROMEO	*ROH* ME OH
S	SIERRA	SEE *AIR* RAH
T	TANGO	*TANG* GO
U	UNIFORM	*YOU* NEE FORM
V	VICTOR	*VIC* TAH
W	WHISKEY	*WISS* KEY
X	X-RAY	*ECKS* RAY
Y	YANKEE	*YANK* KEY
Z	ZULU	*ZOO* LOO

(b) When sending figures:

Number	Pronunciation
0	ZERO
1	WUN
2	TOO
3	THUH-REE
4	FO-WER
5	FI-YIV
6	SIX
7	SEVEN
8	ATE
9	NINER

(c) Telephone numbers:

When quoting telephone numbers it is the practice for Post Office telephone exchange operators to follow the guidance given in the following notes:

(i) Complete hundreds up to 900 and complete thousands up to and including 10 000 are pronounced in the ordinary manner, e.g. *'seven hundred', 'nine thousand'*.

(ii) When pronouncing other numbers, including complete thousands above 10 000;

   (*a*) Three and four figure numbers: a slight pause is made between the 'hundreds' and the 'tens digits';

   (*b*) Five figure numbers: a slight pause is made after the first and third figures;

   (*c*) Six figure numbers: a slight pause is made after the second and fourth figures.

When the same figure occurs twice between the pauses, the word *'double'* is used to combine the pair of figures, but where the pause occurs between the repeated figures, each figure is quoted separately.

Examples:

Numbers	Pronunciation
10	One oh
22	double two
223	two-two three
333	three-double three
0334	oh three-three four
22551	two-two five-five one
44000	four-four oh-double oh
255211	two five-five two-double one

Standard messages

1. Messages from fires and other incidents

(a)   The drafting and despatch of messages from fires and other incidents is a most important aspect of fire service work. Control rooms must be kept regularly advised of information relevant to their mobilising responsibilities, and senior officers have to be kept informed of situations as they develop in order that appropriate action may be initiated by them as necessary.

(b)   In order that the information required by control rooms and senior officers may be drafted and despatched with a minimum of delay, a standard message procedure is adopted which determines not only the message format but also the message content.

(c)   Although there may be local variations of detail to meet the needs of individual brigades, the procedures and examples given in this section of the Drill Book represent the basic principles and general practice and should be particularly useful for recruit training and the Central Training Establishments.

(d)   All personnel should be trained and regularly exercised in the drafting and despatch of standard messages. When drafting messages, brevity and the omission of irrelevant words and phrases is important and only information which is essential to the immediate operational needs of control rooms and senior officers should be included. (Detailed post-incident information such as that required for fire reports or other statistical purposes should not be included in standard messages normally sent by radio during operations.)

(e)   Messages should normally be originated by (or with the authority of) the officer in charge of the incident.

(f)   They should be sent by the quickest available means, e.g. by radio, telephone, vehicle, messenger, etc., as may be appropriate. The officer in charge need not necessarily transmit messages himself, but may delegate this duty to a subordinate. When a control point or control unit is functioning, all messages should be passed to it for transmission and recording.

(g)   Where practicable, messages should be written out before despatch and checked by the originating officer.

(h)   As soon as a message has been sent, the sender should report back to the originating officer, informing him accordingly and repeating the actual wording of the message sent. If such confirmation is not received within a reasonable time, the originating officer should initiate a repeat message clearly prefixed with the word *'duplicate'*.

(j)   Abbreviations should not be used when passing messages orally e.g. 'Water Tenders' should not be transmitted as 'WrT'. The example messages given in this section are set out as they would be spoken.

(k)   The aids towards clearness of speech, as set out in this Drill Book (pages 247–248), should be used when using telephones or radio.

(l)   Any officer taking charge should verify the address of the incident and if necessary send a corrected address message.

2. Assistance messages

An assistance message is a message asking for additional appliances, equipment and/or personnel, or for special information.

(a) Request for additional pumps

A request for additional pumps should always be in the form 'Make pumps...', the figure quoted always including any pumps already in attendance or previously asked for (see paragraph (g) below). Water tenders and pump escapes should normally be regarded as pumps for this purpose, while other special appliances should not.

For example, if the first attendance at a fire consisted of a pump escape and one pump, or a water tender and one pump, and an additional pump was required, the assistance message should be *'Make pumps 3'*. If, however, the attendance were a pump escape, one pump and one turntable ladder-pump, and two more pumps were required, the message should be *'Make pumps 4'*.

> *Note:* Where it is known that persons are trapped or unaccounted for at an incident, the words *'Persons reported'* should be added to the first message back, e.g. *'Make pumps 4. Persons reported'*. If assistance is not considered necessary this information should be sent as an Informative message (see example 4(a)).

(b) Request for Special Appliance

When asking for a special appliance the form of the request will depend upon whether an appliance of the type required (i) is being requested for the first time, or (ii) is already in attendance or has been previously requested. For (i) the request should be in the form *'Two salvage tenders required'*. For (ii) it should be in the form *'Make salvage tenders 2.'*

(c) Request for additional pumps, and for special appliances of a type not previously asked for

'From Sub-Officer Jones at 10 High Street, Banktown. Make pumps 3. Turntable ladder required.'

(d) Request for additional pumps, additional special appliances, and special appliances of a type not previously asked for

'From Station Officer Green at 19 Allen Road. Make pumps 6 and emergency tenders 2. Turntable ladder and ambulance required.'

(e) Request for additional pumps for use in connection with a Water Relay.

'From Station Officer...at...Make pumps 6, including 3 for water relaying.'

(f) Message from an officer in charge of an appliance involved in a collision en route to an incident asking for assistance.

'From Sub-Officer Smith. Pump B2 Hallam involved in collision junction Allen Road and High Street. Unable to proceed. Member of public/brigade injured. Ambulance/breakdown lorry required. Telephone contact Hallam 21345.'

(g) Subsequent Assistance Messages

A developing fire situation may make it necessary to send further assistance messages. The number of additional appliances should then be added to the total requested in the previous message. For example, if the first assistance message was *'Make pumps 5'* and a further five pumps were found to be needed, the subsequent assistance message should state *'Make pumps 10'*. If it were then found necessary to request a further five pumps, the next assistance message should state *'Make pumps 15'*.

(h) Request for attendance of a Public Utility representative.

When it is necessary for the urgent attendance of public utility representatives to render assistance at an incident, an assistance message should be sent. For example *'From Station Officer Blank at 19 Allen Road. Gas Board required to shut off supply.'*

(j) Request for Information

When an officer in charge requires information to assist him in dealing with an incident, an assistance message should be sent. For example *'From Station Officer White at High Street, Blanktown. Spillage of sulphuric acid from overturned tanker. Request information.'*

3. Informative messages

An informative message is a message giving details of an incident and/or the progress of operations. Wherever lives are endangered, a message to that effect should be sent back at once (see paragraphs 2(a) and 4(a)). All other informative messages should be sent back as soon as practicable; the first message giving the following information in the order shown:

(a) If a building:

(i)   The correct address.

(ii)   The use to which the building is put, unless the character of it is well known, e.g. the Town Hall.

(iii) The height of the building (expressed in terms of the number of floors) and the approximate area of the site which it covers (expressed in terms of frontage and depth in metres).

(iv) The part of the building which is involved.

(v)   What is in use e.g. 2 jets/4 breathing apparatus.

A building comprising ground, first and second floors should be described as *'a building of three floors'*. Basements should not be included unless they are involved or likely to become involved, in which case the description should be *'a building of three floors with basement and sub-basement'*.

The approximate area of the building should be stated in the form *'...metres by...metres'*. Buildings of a special or unusual type, such as oast houses, silos, transformer stations, etc, should be identified by the name by which they are commonly known, e.g. *'a dutch barn 30 m by 10 m'*; *'a railway signal box 10 m by 5 m'*; *'a range of buildings of two, three and four floors covering area of 100 m by 25 m.'*

The location of the fire or other incident should be described by reference to the floor or floors involved, e.g. *'first floor alight'* (meaning the floor above the ground floor).

(b) If a Ship:

(i)   Type (i.e. whether steamship, motor vessel, sailing ship, tanker, barge, etc.)

(ii)   Name

(iii) Where lying

(iv) Gross tonnage

(v)   Cargo

(vi) Location and approximate extent of fire

(vii) What is in use e.g. 2 jets/8 breathing apparatus

(c) If property other than a building or a ship
Such details of the fire or other incident as will give a concise description of the property involved and what is in use.

The approximate areas covered by fires in woodland, heath, crops, etc, may be given either in hectares or square kilometres or indicated by the approximate length and breadth of the area involved in metres or kilometres as appropriate.

(d) General
If all the above information cannot be obtained quickly, that which is readily available should be sent, leaving corrections or additional particulars to be sent in later messages.

Subsequent informative messages should advise progress of operations for the information of control rooms and senior officers. Generally, such messages should be sent at intervals of not more than half an hour. Brief particulars of the damage and of any rescues effected should be included. (See paragraph 5. 'Stop messages'.)

4. Examples of informative messages

(a) *'From Station Officer Jones at Queen's Hotel, Bilton. Persons reported.*

(b) *'From Station Officer Black at 28 Corporation Street. Furniture Store. Seven Floors. 50 m by 20 m. Three upper floors alight. 4 jets/6 breathing apparatus in use.'*

(c) *'From Station Officer Jones at Queens Hotel. Six floors about 60 m by 40 m. Two upper floors alight. 4 jets/4 breathing apparatus in use.' All persons accounted for.*

(d) *'...Paint store. Four floors, basement and sub-basement about 30 m by 20 m. Basement and sub-basement alight. 2 jets/6 breathing apparatus in use.'*

(e) *'From Station Officer Brown at 16 Smith Street. Fire not yet located. Breathing appartus in use.'*

(f) *'From Divisional Officer Green at 28 Corporation Street. Fire surrounded.'*

(g) *'From Station Officer Gray at SS Galvanic at Pilots' jetty. Vessel of 8000 tonnes laden with general cargo. Numbers one and two holds alight. 2 jets/8 breathing apparatus in use.'*

(h) *'From Sub-Officer Rose at 12 High Street. Building collapsed, persons trapped. Cutting set and crane in use.'*

(j)   'From Station Officer Smith on M3 Motorway at Southwood. Multiple crash on southbound carriageway. Extrication of trapped casualties proceeding. Police and ambulances in attendance.'

(k)   'From Station Officer Green at Napsbury Railway Station. Southbound passenger train derailed. 4 coaches overturned down embankment persons trapped. Rescue operations proceeding.'

5. Stop messages

A stop message (the words 'Stop for . . . ' followed by the *address of the incident*) indicates that no more help is required and that the personnel and appliances already in attendance or requested are sufficient, except for any necessary reliefs. A stop message should be sent from every incident as soon as it is certain that no further assistance is needed. Stop messages may, according to individual brigade practice, be either (i) confined to the words 'Stop for. . . ' (*address only*), or (ii) they may include other brief information, as follows.

When a Stop message follows an Informative message, a repeat of the description details is unnecessary, but the number of jets and/or equipment in use may be included if they have changed since the last informative message, e.g. 'Stop for . . . (address). . . 6 jets'. For small fires the Stop message may be combined with an informative message, e.g. 'Stop for . . . address. . . Garage 13 m by 10 m at rear. Hose reel'.

When persons have been reported trapped or unaccounted for, it is not always possible to sent the message 'All persons accounted for' before the 'Stop' message. Where appropriate the words should be added at the end of the 'Stop' message, e.g. 'Stop for Queen's Hotel, Bilton. Back room top floor damaged. Two hose reels. All persons accounted for.' If there is a doubt that persons may still be unaccounted for when the 'Stop' is sent back, the words 'All persons not yet accounted for due to . . . . (insert reason e.g. building collapsed). Subsequently, when they have been accounted for, a further informative should also be sent.

6. Sequence of messages

Following routine *'mobile'* and *'in attendance'* messages (where used) the sequence of messages would normally be as follows.

(a) Assistance message
(b) Informative message
(c) Further assistance messages and informative messages, as necessary
(d) Fire surrounded message
(e) Stop message
(f) Further informative messages as necessary

7. Coded messages

The introduction of radio data transmission systems can facilitate the introduction of a limited range of coded messages (e.g. *'Available at station'*, *'Available on radio'*, *'Not available'*, *'Arrived at incident'*, *'Stop'*, etc.)

Additionally a number of brigades have devised coded message systems for verbal transmission of messages similar to those mentioned above.

Printed for Her Majesty's Stationery Office by Commercial Colour Press, London E7.
1/86, C100, Dd.738796.